HAPPY TO 102

The Best Kept Secrets to a Long and Happy Life

Kathy N. Johnson, PhD, CMC
James H. Johnson, PhD
Lily Sarafan, MS

HappyTo102.com

ISBN 978-0-615-28194-0

ACKNOWLEDGMENTS

To the centenarians around the world who inspire us.
To the seniors throughout North America we feel privileged to serve each day.

TABLE OF CONTENTS

INTRODUCTION

Everybody knows that people will live a lot longer in the future. But most of us don't know exactly what we mean by "a lot longer." Brace yourself, because the truth will surprise you. According to the Census Bureau, in 50 years more than 1 million Americans will live past the age of 102! The trend continues in Canada and across the globe. This means that most of us alive today have a very real chance of living to 102. And even those of us who don't make it to 102 will probably live nearly a decade longer than the previous generation.

So that's the good news.

Now let's talk about the bad news. Scientists have long noticed that happy people live longer, but just because we live longer doesn't mean that we will automatically live happier or healthier. Many long lived seniors will suffer from frailty or chronic illness that makes life difficult. That is, unless they proactively prevent this state of affairs from occurring.

The implications of the coming changes in lifespan are enormous – much greater than you would ever guess.

Here's why ...

As important as it is to live a long time, it is probably more important to live happily and well. And to live happily, seniors need to plan to live to 102 years of age, rather than planning to live to 80 or 90. In other words, people need to accept the idea of living to 102 as the new norm and forget the old idea of dying around age 87.

Seniors younger than 87 need to think, act and live young. Rather than preparing to die early, they need to be prepared to live long and well. There's time enough to think old when they are past 100. And...

**Since seniors are going to live long, they might
as well live well during their older years!**

The 70 year old senior planning to live to 102 will do things differently than the one planning to live to 75. And there is a good reason for this. Seniors expecting to live past 102 know that they have at least 30% of their life still ahead! Consequently, they need to think about how to enjoy life rather than prepare for death.

What today's senior needs to be concerned about

First, today's senior absolutely wants to maintain an independent lifestyle. In a recent survey of American centenarians, 81% cited "maintaining a sense of independence" as a very important key to their life happiness. Of course, the easiest way to maintain a sense of independence is for seniors to continue living as they have always lived: in their own home, among their own things and with their own way of doing things.

The most important threat to maintaining independence throughout life is the inability to accomplish routine activities of daily living because of physical changes or poor health. So expect today's senior to exercise, get regular check-ups and to concentrate on personal health.

However, even if a senior is frail or has a chronic illness, it does not have to mean the loss of personal independence. Most seniors can retain independence with the help of outside caregivers. True! Frail or chronically ill seniors often find it difficult to complete previously routine tasks such as getting in and out of a bathtub or cooking dinner for themselves. But being frail isn't nearly the same thing as having a terminal illness – anymore than being a helpless infant is a terminal problem.

What seniors need in order to continue to stay in their own home is someone to "seniorize" their home with appropriate safety devices and modifications. Plus, they need someone to help them with tasks that are difficult or impossible to accomplish without assistance.

For most seniors, having someone help with basic tasks makes all the difference between a comfortable, easy life and a trying, painful one. Remember, just because a person becomes too frail or too forgetful to manage a few basic tasks does not cause them to have to stop living independently.

In order to live to 102 and beyond, today's senior must recognize that increasing frailties are a part of living a long time. At a minimum, seniors must pay attention to four of the most basic difficulties associated with growing older.

- **Safety** requires the home to be suitably designed and maintained to minimize the possibility of falling. Also, the risk of fire, crime or medical emergency needs to be controlled.
- **Proper nutrition** needs to be assured, through healthy shopping, cooking and eating.
- **Transportation** must be easily accessible or provided, especially once seniors become unable to drive safely.

- **Social life** remains a crucial element in the health and longevity of seniors. It is essential for minimizing despair, depression and thoughts of death.

Remember that these are *life* concerns and not *medical* concerns. In the past, we have been too quick to "medicalize" the frailties that are simply a part of growing old. But old age is not a medical event. It is one in which the body and mind are changing. So our thinking about the new senior lifestyle must also change.

The good news here is that we already have a comprehensive senior support system in place to help with issues related to the new longer lifespan. This broad spectrum of support includes home care, professional geriatric care managers, senior centers, elder attorneys, trust managers, physicians, hospital sitters, discharge planners, rehabilitation centers, assisted living facilities, visiting nurses, psychology professionals, social workers and others. This diverse network can expertly address the unique physical, mental, social, and emotional issues related to growing older and embracing a changing lifespan.

Aging independently, at home with the help of a large, extended, senior support system is a new concept for many seniors and their families. Until about twenty years ago, community based support for seniors was virtually non-existent in most parts of North America. Now, when seniors need help they have something they never had before: a choice that doesn't force them to leave their homes and become dependent upon outside settings. And one that doesn't force them to rely exclusively on children and relatives.

Now seniors can live graciously as long as they plan their lives around the prospect of living to 102 and beyond. But it all begins with the individual. Seniors themselves need to learn and accept —and feel entitled to—the best options available.

Living to 102—and loving it

Medical science and quality of life have extended the modern lifespan beyond the expectations of any previous generation. We've all been granted an extended lease on life. So how do we make the most of this? In the following chapters, you'll learn about the choices you can make to not only improve your chances of living to 102, but also to enjoy a better quality of life as you get there. To your health and happiness now and at 102!

ONE

Daylight Savings Time for the Twilight Years

We are living through a time of vast change. Within the last fifty years, modern medicine and abundant nutrition have extended not just the number of years you can live, but the quality of life you can enjoy. Now most people can expect to live between 85 and 100 years. That's about 15 years longer than the lifespan expected just a half century ago. By the middle of this century, demographers say one in fifty women (and one in two hundred men) will live to age 100 or more.

Expect to see bigger birthday cakes or thinner candles in the decades ahead. It's time to stop thinking of the golden years as a scary precipice and instead consider them as just a part of our normal lifespan.

Seniors need to acknowledge that with advanced age comes physical frailty. They also need to acknowledge that chronic illness is more common in older adults. Whether a senior enjoys the later part of life depends greatly on the ability to live independently at home with a normal lifestyle – in spite of frailty or chronic illness. That's why in-home care is becoming increasingly more important as people live longer.

Ask yourself, "Will I be happy with my style of living during my older years – even if I'm bound to have frailties and illnesses?"

The answer will depend largely upon you and your surroundings. If you move into some form of shared housing, your lifestyle will drastically change.

On the other hand, for those of you who live to 102 and continue to reside in your own home, remaining active and doing what you have always done, the odds are good that you will continue to enjoy life. That, in a nutshell, is why in-home care is such an important idea – now and for the future.

What's most important in later years?

American Perceptions of Aging in the 21st Century, a 25-year study by the National Council on Aging (NCOA), examined the myths and realities of the aging experience in America. In this study people were surveyed about how they feel and what they are doing in preparation for old age. When 65 and 70 year olds were asked if they would be happy to live another ten years, only 7 percent said they would be unhappy. Problems that seniors identified as most serious included fears regarding health, crime, money and loneliness.

When asked about their greatest worries for old age the majority of people (60 percent) ranked memory loss as their top fear. At a secondary level, more than half were "very worried or somewhat worried" about long term care costs. The least of their worries was about outliving their pension and savings. The surprise comes in learning what people viewed as most important in terms of preparations for later life. Three quarters of respondents ranked "Establishing a Living Will" and having "Savings" as their top priorities, whereas "Health Habits" and "Long Term Care Insurance" were rated significantly lower. While half of respondents said they worry that they won't be able to afford long-term care, they rated long term care insurance as their lowest priority.

Furthermore, even in later years, a person's health habits are what impact memory and health most. At this time, long term care insurance is the only kind of coverage that will pay for in-home care, the kind of care that enables seniors with memory loss and other chronic health problems to live independently.

The answer behind this dichotomy lies in the value seniors place on their savings compared to the value they place on themselves. Many people who are now in their 80s are used to living frugally and saving as much as possible, desiring to leave a legacy to their children, suggests Emily Saltz, Licensed Independent Clinical Social Worker and the director of Elder Resources, a private geriatric care management firm in Newton, Massachusetts.

Also, for seniors to receive the care they deserve, their children need to avoid any disparity in the value they place on the life of their parents as compared with the life of their children. Most parents want only the best for their kids. (Seeking out the cheapest babysitter or the cheapest college for their son or daughter doesn't even enter their mind.) By contrast, when it comes to senior care, finding the least expensive solution sometimes becomes a family focus. Families often believe that the most cost-effective solution is the best solution.

But this should not be surprising because even trusted information sources such as Consumer Reports focus on money rather than quality of life when it comes to senior care. Take for example their Complete Guide to Health Services for Seniors—the

Introduction says that the book is designed to answer all the most important questions pertaining to senior living. It turns out that half of these questions are about how to save money on senior care. The first chapter of this compendium is a virtual bible about how to cut costs when it comes to the care of your parents. It's got sections entitled "Sticker Shock" and "Talking about Money." The first paragraph alone mentions money 5 times.

In our current age where people live into the hundreds it doesn't make sense to think of life in terms of thrift and low cost senior warehousing. Rather it makes sense to think about making life more productive and enjoyable. It's a new age and it's time for some new thinking.

Changing the perspective on aging

In the past retirement age has been about stopping. Now it needs to be about going. The senior years should not be an excuse for anything, let alone abandoning life.

Our population is growing older at the fastest pace in history. In most of North America, the number of seniors aged 65 and older will exceed the number of children under the age of 15 by 2015. By 2031, every baby boomer—a generation that numbers 80 million—will be over age 65. The oldest boomers will be 88. By then, seniors will account for fully one quarter of the North American population.

These changing demographics, combined with the increasing human lifespan, make it necessary to re-evaluate how society thinks about old age. For example, in many parts of Asia, octogenarians (eighties) and nonagenarians (nineties) have traditionally been viewed as jewels of society and proud symbols of the country. Western society is finally letting go of its past-tense view of seniors as people who have "had their time." Seniors are regaining their status as extremely valuable members of the community.

A 2001 survey by Erdman Palmore revealed that 31 percent of respondents over 65 reported being ignored or not taken seriously because of their age. "As we age, we crave the same respect and consideration that we garnered in our adult years," says Dr. Robert N. Butler of the International Longevity Center. "We must work together as a society to promote positive attitudes and portrayals of older people. We must not fail to respect and protect the rights of older people."

There has been recent success in stopping negative age stereotypes that used to be prevalent in movies and television. At a 2003 Senate hearing on ageism, Doris Roberts, the Emmy-award winning actress in her seventies from the television show Everybody Loves Raymond, testified against inaccurate media portrayals of the elderly. "My peers and I are portrayed as dependent, helpless, unproductive and demanding rather than deserving," Roberts testified. "In reality, the majority of seniors are self-sufficient, middle-class consumers with more assets than most young people, and with time and talent to offer society."

Government officials would do well to heed what seniors say. People 65 and older are by far the most prolific voters in North America. In the 2004 United States Presidential election, over 70 percent of people over age 65 voted. Currently, more than one in every five votes is cast by someone 65 or older, and their numbers are continuing to rise faster than any other group of voters. It's also essential for seniors to have a positive view of themselves. In a longevity study conducted by Yale University, following 660 people age 50 and older, those with more positive self-perceptions about aging lived 7.5 years longer than those with negative self-perceptions of aging. People's own positive attitudes toward old age appear to boost their mental health in later years. The results of the study also indicated that seniors who identify with positive stereotypes about aging had significantly better memory and balance, whereas negative self-perceptions contributed to worse memory, feelings of worthlessness and even greater susceptibility to falls.

Getting sensitive about seniors

"We need to raise the consciousness of the need for incorporating content on aging into all levels of schools' curricula," says Forrest Scogin, chairman of the American Psychology Association's Committee on Aging. "They are a diverse group. Stereotypes just don't work."

Fortunately, education has a proven impact on younger people's attitudes toward seniors. In a 2005 study by the School of Family and Consumer Sciences at Eastern Illinois University, psychologists sought to determine the influence of college courses on attitude change toward older adults. Findings revealed that students' negative attitudes toward older adults significantly decreased and their positive attitudes increased after taking a course on Aging and Family.

Gerontologists have been making great strides in "age sensitivity training." Several universities now include courses on aging— intended for liberal arts undergraduates, not just students of gerontology or health care. Monika Wood, a sociology professor at Rutgers University in New Jersey, even administers an "aging simulation" regimen in her courses. "Reading about aging is not the same as experiencing it," Wood says. She requires her students to alter their clothing and wear various accessories that simulate the aches and pains, diminished senses and restricted movements experienced by seniors. Special glasses simulate the visual impairment of cataracts, glaucoma or macular degeneration. Dried corn kernels in the shoes re-create the pain of walking. Rubber gloves and duct taped elbows, knees and knuckles impart the limited range of motion from arthritis. Ear plugs and nose plugs convey the loss of hearing and taste that sometimes accompany old age. These aging simulation exercises don't strive just to teach, but to instill empathy in the students.

Why a little help makes such a big difference

Empathy for seniors includes understanding that even simple, daily tasks can become extremely difficult if you become frail. Most of us think of ourselves—and our parents—as always being strong, capable and self-sufficient. It's difficult to imagine ever needing help with physical activities we currently take for granted, especially when this growing need comes on gradually. It takes surprisingly little incapacity to begin a downward spiral that can lead to serious ramifications. An increasing fear of driving, perhaps too embarrassing to mention even to a friend or family member, turns shopping for groceries into a difficult ordeal. This, combined with a loss of appetite, leads to poor nutrition. Without eating, there's no energy for activity or exercise. Idle, undernourished bones and muscles weaken. A fall may ensue and the consequences can be disastrous.

It's often hard to see such subtle changes, especially when family members don't live together. Over the years of short phone calls, occasional letters and infrequent visits, plenty can go unmentioned and unnoticed. Suddenly, the holidays come and you get to spend more time together. That's when many people first notice their parents aren't doing so well. They see that their parents aren't Super Mom or Super Dad after all. Rather they are humans who are getting older and may now need help with everyday tasks.

It's a common occurrence that when a senior's spouse dies, he or she dies soon after. This pattern plays in countless families across North America. Most people accept this without question, believing the romantic notion that the lingering spouse died of a broken heart, longing to be united with his or her partner. More often, the sad reality is that the swift passage of these surviving spouses may have been due to the fact that their sole caregiver was the one who died first, leaving them not only grieving, but incapable of caring for their own daily needs—unable to clean or cook for themselves, without companionship and without anyone to monitor their medications and safety.

As a matter of fact, almost two-thirds of the time, it's the caregiving spouse who dies first. As reported in the Journal of the American Medical Association, elderly spousal caregivers (aged 66-96) experiencing caregiver strain have a 63 percent higher mortality rate than non-caregivers of the same age. That's even after adjusting for socio-demographic factors, prevalent disease and cardiovascular disease. On the other hand, having an extra caregiver on hand—even on an occasional basis—can greatly relieve the stress endured by the primary family caregiver, reducing mortality significantly.

Aging gracefully doesn't mean aging silently

Families can't always count on knowing when seniors need a little help. Sometimes doing what's best means persuading them to accept assistance when they don't necessarily want it. Getting help is easy—from senior centers to professional geriatric care managers to in-home caregivers and more. Getting your parents —or yourself—to accept help is often the most difficult step.

Often adult children of elderly parents notice small changes in their Mom or Dad: a bruise or wound from a fall, not bathing regularly, weight loss or forgetting simple directions. The typical answer when confronting our parents is 'Oh everything is fine, I don't need any help, don't worry about me!' Losing one's independence is hard to accept without swallowing a bit of pride. That's why it is essential to share an understanding that the only way that one's independence can be maintained is by depending on some outside help—especially as age progresses.

Parents commonly resist the notion that they need to be taken care of—especially by their children. Many seniors are reluctant to spend money on something as "frivolous" as having someone drive, clean house or prepare meals for them. While this type of assistance may seem like a luxurious extravagance to some, the longer one lives, the more these become necessities.

As seniors grow older, they need to understand that they don't just need such help. Rather, they are worth it and deserve it! Everyone has one life to live. The fact that life can be longer than anyone thought possible makes it all the more important that it be lived to the maximum.

REMEMBER...

Whether a senior enjoys the later part of life depends greatly on the ability to live independently at home with a normal lifestyle. That's why in-home care is becoming increasingly more important as people live longer.

TWO
Independence, Interdependence—and Upon What They Depend

One way to gauge the ability to live independently is to consider the ability to drive. As a teenager you gain independence when you start to drive, and as a senior you start to lose independence when you can no longer drive. But having your own personal driver changes these guidelines significantly—especially for seniors. In real life seniors can retain their independence many years after they stop driving as long as they have someone who can drive for them.

Until recently, the peak time for losing independence (and loss of independent driving) occurred around the age of 80. This was mainly due to loss of driving ability, but it was also due to physical and/or mental losses associated with older age. Now, it is recognized that the decision regarding independence is based more on social beliefs than it is about physical deficits associated with older age. Most seniors can retain their functional independence for years past the time that they cease driving.

Becoming dependent on others is life changing for many older adults. Seniors often believe that losing personal autonomy is tantamount to reducing their lifespans. So it's no wonder that the vast majority of seniors fear losing their independence as much as they fear death! Fortunately, there is seldom a reason that any senior needs to live a life of total helplessness and dependence. In fact, the more natural course of life is to preserve our independence at any age.

Senior advocacy groups and home care associations are consistent in their support of independence for the senior population. After all, it's easy to rally around images of centenarians playing tennis or traveling the world, living as independently as they did in their fifties. Independence, however, does not necessarily mean seniors will be just as active and agile as they were in their younger years. It simply means they will live life as freely and self-governing as is possible, given their personal circumstances. Independent living does not necessarily mean doing everything yourself. Instead, it means being in control of how and when things are done.

The truth is that society is changing its perception that independent seniors are just a small subset of the larger 85 and up population. Instead society is moving toward the idea that all seniors deserve and can lead dignified, self-governing lives in almost any state of physical or mental ability.

But still, too many of us believe the age-old cliché that parent-child roles are automatically reversed as parents age. This doesn't have to be true! Social support and home care should not be confused with parenting. The best way to break this cycle is to keep seniors in the home environment they are already most familiar with, where there is the greatest likelihood of preserving the routines and relationships they have become accustomed to over a lifetime. In their homes, seniors are in greater control of their schedules, lifestyle and happiness.

The argument has been made that a lifestyle of happiness and longevity necessitates a certain level of independence. So let's discuss what independence looks like for seniors and how it can be achieved. But first, let's shift the discussion from independence to a more holistic approach, interdependence.

It is interdependence that we should strive to achieve

Interdependence is a dynamic of being mutually responsible to and sharing a common set of principles with others. It can also be defined as the interconnectedness and the reliance on one another socially, economically, environmentally and politically.

Interdependence, then, is the foundation for keeping seniors at home, where home care agencies, care managers and family members work together to provide the most productive and comfortable environment for a senior. It is a relationship of working together rather than a "one-sided" dependence that is important to consider here.

Of course, none of us wants to be helpless or dependent on others. So here are some things to keep in mind to preserve independence (and achieve interdependence) for the seniors in your life.

- **Movement** – Walking and stretching should be incorporated into a senior's daily life as long as these exercises don't cause pain. Exercise is key to maintaining circulation and bone density in seniors.
- **Encourage Social Engagement** – Seniors can become empowered through participation. Whether sharing life stories for a grandchild's school project or establishing a weekly session with friends, engaging with others can significantly increase a senior's self-esteem and sense of independence.

- **Ask for A Senior's Advice** – Take advantage of the life experiences that seniors have. Solicit their advice around real issues. Don't be afraid to thank them for their input. Make sure to take at least some of their advice.
- **Nutrition** – Muscle loss is an inevitable consequence of aging, but incorporating adequate amounts of protein and vitamins into the diet can actually help the body make muscle. (More about this later.)
- **Consider Professional Caregivers for Companionship** – For seniors who live alone, isolation is an unfortunate aspect of their daily lives. A companion can help keep their memories sharp and bring an uplifting spirit to what otherwise might be a monotonous and lonely routine.

Interdependence includes participation of players and systems that are already in place and utilized in all other phases of our lives. Together we can achieve the critical paradigm shift from dependence to practical interdependence for seniors.

Declaration of Interdependence

We already have in place compassionate, professional experts in our communities throughout North America and across the globe that are on-call and prepared to help seniors and their families achieve interdependence. We do not need to invent the positions that will support a lifestyle of interdependence, nor do we need to establish new tools. From birth to old age, we live in an interdependent community in which parents, nannies, neighbors, relatives, friends and colleagues make up the support system we each depend on. There is no justifiable reason for modifying our lifestyle drastically just because we require some personal assistance in our later years.

When our children need help, we employ all available resources while offering them the freedom and comfort of a warm and consistent home environment meant to inspire happiness and longevity. What is exciting about the prospect of interdependence for seniors, then, is that we are actually relying on long-standing values and principles that we already act on in every other phase of our lives.

Keep in mind that we may need to change our views to accommodate the reality that men and women of any age can take advantage of the interdependent communities we've relied on throughout our lives in order to live long, fulfilling lives. Independence may not mean running a marathon for many, but it means relying on all the support systems we already have in place to ensure the highest quality of life, no matter what our age.

REMEMBER...

Independent living does not necessarily mean doing everything yourself: It means being in control of how and when things are done. From birth to old age, we live and thrive in interdependent communities; there is no justifiable reason for modifying our lifestyle drastically just because we require some personal assistance in our later years. Make a Declaration of Interdependence for yourself or the seniors in your life!

THREE
You Age What You Eat

This is the first of two chapters devoted to appropriate nutrition for seniors. In this chapter we talk about contemporary thinking on what is the best diet for seniors. This information is based on nutritional research and provides a basic primer for seniors and their families on the healthiest approach to eating. In a later chapter we will discuss diet as part of a more holistic lifestyle program called the Balanced Care Method™.

The Balanced Care Method™ is based on scientific research on the island of Okinawa (a part of Japan). Okinawa is famous for having more centenarians per capita than any other place on Earth. Not surprisingly, it has become the focus of a large scale international study to look at why this occurs. Results from this research are presented in a later chapter.

That being said, let's begin by discussing general issues about nutrition that seniors need to know. When we come back to the topic of what we can learn from the Okinawans about living the longest and healthiest possible life, we will attempt to place all of this within the concept of a "best practices" lifestyle for seniors.

Let's start by acknowledging that good nutrition is important for everybody. And while seniors often need to eat less than they did when they were younger, the quality of the food they eat and its nutritional value are even more essential. Older bodies decline swiftly without ample building blocks. Seniors are especially susceptible to serious malnutrition, for several reasons. The first and most important reason is that the senses of smell and taste decline with age, causing seniors to take less pleasure in eating. Second, seniors tend to lose their physical appetite, eating less food and eating less often. Third, dementia, frailty and poor mobility make it difficult to prepare meals, let alone go shopping for food. Finally, these three factors are complicated by the fact that as people get older they cannot absorb, process or store vitamins, minerals or protein as easily. With few nutritional elements in reserve, the human body actually starts to digest itself for sustenance—exponentially hastening its decline.

The older seniors get, the less they need to eat compared to when they were younger and more active. However, as they age, the quality of the food they eat becomes increasingly more important. (Everyone should ignore the occasional news story about some centenarian in the Adirondacks who claims that the secret to his longevity is smoking cigars and eating one cupcake per day.) Living independently and happily to 102 is a much more likely outcome if you follow the advice gleaned from the bounty of scientific studies on nutrition. We've distilled a lot of these findings into the following encapsulated suggestions, in hopes you'll find them easier to swallow.

7 super foods that prolong life

Results of recent long-term research studies have pointed to a number of nutrients that many seniors lack, but are especially valuable for senior living. Here are seven "super foods" that are loaded with these essential nutrients. Some of the foods on this list may even surprise you.

1. Salmon or other fatty fish

Salmon and other cold water fish, such as tuna, sardines or mackerel are low in calories and saturated fat, yet high in protein. Most important, these fish are rich in a unique type of health-promoting fat, the essential fatty acid, DHA (docosahexaenoic acid), better known as omega-3.

Omega-3 essential fatty acid optimizes levels of triglycerides which carry fat in your bloodstream, reducing the low density LDL (bad) cholesterol linked to increased risk of cardiovascular disease, while improving the high HDL (good) cholesterol that fights deposits in the arteries. There is strong evidence linking low levels of DHA to memory loss and other symptoms of dementia. A 10-year study of 1,000 older individuals showed that a low DHA level was a significant risk factor for the onset of Alzheimer's disease *(Archives of Neurology)*.

Why not just take fish oil supplements? Norwegian researchers studied the absorption of omega-3 from salmon compared to fish oil capsules and found that enjoying salmon or tuna just twice per week raised blood levels of omega-3 even more effectively than taking daily fish oil supplements.

Not all fish is good for you. Tilapia has increased in popularity in recent years, due to its easy cultivation and low price. Unfortunately, scientists have found that Tilapia is not the healthy fish it was once assumed to be. Surprising new research (July 2008) found that Tilapia is potentially dangerous to eat. Researchers from Wake Forest University School of Medicine warn that farm-raised Tilapia has very low levels of beneficial omega-3 fatty acids and, perhaps worse, very high levels of omega-6 fatty acids. The scientists say the combination could be a potentially dangerous food source for some patients, mostly seniors, with heart disease, arthritis, asthma and other allergic and auto-immune diseases that are particularly vulnerable to an "exaggerated inflammatory response." Omega-6 oils can also increase chances of memory problems, as found in a 2007 study of seniors.

What about mercury? Although much bad press has hounded the high levels of mercury in certain fish, mercury should be of very little concern to seniors. That's because mercury's major threat (according to a 2004 report by the Food and Drug Administration) is that it accumulates within women's ovaries, increasing the risk of brain-related birth defects in their children. Over the age of menopause, women (as well as older men) have little to fear from mercury—especially compared to the beneficial health effects of eating fatty fish.

2. Walnuts, almonds or other nuts

Considerable scientific evidence suggests that eating one ounce per day of certain nuts may reduce the risk of heart disease. In 2003, the Food and Drug Administration (FDA) approved this claim exclusively for walnuts, almonds, hazelnuts, pecans, pistachios and peanuts. Although nuts are a higher-fat food, they are cholesterol-free. Most of their fat comes from heart-healthy unsaturated fat, including omega-3. In fact, one ounce of walnuts (about a handful) is all that is needed to meet the daily omega-3 dietary recommendation by the National Academies' Institute of Medicine.

Walnuts and other nuts (especially Brazil nuts) are also one of the best sources for what scientists have called the top three nutritional deficiencies: magnesium, manganese and selenium. These play a role in more than 100 biochemical reactions in the human body, including critical heart and nerve functions. One ounce of nuts also provides 35 percent of the recommended dietary allowance (RDA) for vitamin E. A study reported in the Journal of the American Medical Association suggests vitamin E may help protect people against Alzheimer's. (Incidentally, the study also found vitamin E in the form of supplements was not associated with a reduction in the risk of Alzheimer's disease.) Walnuts are also recommended as part of the DASH diet (Dietary Approaches to Stop Hypertension), a dietary plan clinically proven to significantly reduce blood pressure.

3. A carrot a day for vitamin A

According to Mary O'Brien, MD, in Alzheimer's: Prevention of the Disease and Other Dementias, "The idea that eating a carrot a day over a lifetime may preserve cognitive function in later years deserves considerable attention." Here's why carrots are garnering attention in Alzheimer's research: Oxidative damage to brain cells contributes to neurological degeneration and the development of dementia. That's why anti-oxidants such as vitamins A (beta-carotene), C, E and flavonoids are so important —especially for seniors. Many complementary studies have shown that individuals that consume higher levels of Vitamin A and other anti-oxidants over several years have substantially decreased levels of Alzheimer's disease.

Carrots make more than just brain food. "Did you know why they say carrots are great for your eyesight?" as the old joke goes, "That's why you never see a rabbit wearing glasses!" The ancient legend about carrots being good for eye health recently got some scientific validation. A new Dutch study links diets rich in four antioxidants—beta-carotene, vitamin C, vitamin E and zinc—to lower odds of developing age-related macular degeneration. Nothing beats a carrot as a powerful source of beta-carotene (which your body converts to vitamin A). One carrot (7 1/2" long) delivers 203 percent of the daily RDA for vitamin A. Broccoli and other vegetables are also high in vitamin A, but you would have to eat almost nine broccoli spears to equal the vitamin A in one carrot. Don't over do it, though. More than three carrots a day will saturate the body's ability to store vitamin A over a short time and can show up as an orange tint on the skin. Also, excessive levels of vitamin A have been linked to an increased risk of hip fracture.

Because many seniors may have difficulty chewing, it's recommended to microwave or lightly steam vegetables to soften them while minimizing the loss of nutrients. Use as little water as possible when cooking. Other beta-carotene/vitamin A powerhouses include sweet potatoes, cantaloupe, mangoes and apricots.

4. Eggs—including the yolk, no joke

Eggs are a superior source of protein, containing all the essential amino acids needed by the human body. On the scale most commonly used for assessing protein, egg is at the highest point, 100, and is used as the standard against which all other foods are assessed. Eggs contain most of the vitamins—except vitamin C—and minerals that the human body requires for health. In particular, eggs are an excellent source of iodine (essential for the thyroid), phosphorus and calcium (required for bone health) and zinc (needed for wound healing and fighting infection).

Although eggs contain cholesterol, eating eggs in moderation won't adversely affect the blood cholesterol level of most people. Cholesterol levels are far more influenced by the amount of saturated and trans fat you eat than your consumption of dietary cholesterol. As Dietitian Nicole Senior notes in her book, Heart Food and Eat to Beat Cholesterol, "Everyone can enjoy eggs in moderation (around 3-4 eggs a week) in the context of a heart-friendly diet." Egg yolks also contain lecithin (phospholipids) which is a natural emulsifier and may reduce cholesterol absorption. You can also find eggs that have been fortified with DHA (omega-3).

To keep eggs healthy for the heart, they should be prepared using non-oily methods of cooking, such as hard- or soft-boiling or poaching. If you prefer fried or scrambled eggs, use olive oil or an olive-oil based spread or cooking spray instead of butter or trans-fatty margarine.

5. Flax seeds

Flax seeds contain high levels of lignin and omega-3 fatty acids. Lignin may benefit the heart and possess anti-cancer properties. Laboratory studies have found reduced growth in specific types of tumors. Flax may also lessen the severity of diabetes by stabilizing blood-sugar levels. Flax seed is also useful as a natural laxative due to its high, soluble (non-gassy) dietary fiber content. You can include flax seed in home cooking by sprinkling it on salads, meats and more. Flax seed mixture can even be substituted for eggs in home baking such as muffins and pancakes. (One tablespoon milled flax seed plus 3 tablespoons water = 1 egg. However, final products will be less fluffy.)

A word of caution about flax: because of the high fiber content, flax seeds and other foods with laxative properties may interfere with the absorption of some medications, so be sure to check with your doctor before including flax in your diet. Also, women undergoing treatment for a cancer that is estrogen-mediating, like breast cancer, should avoid flax, soy or other foods rich in phytoestrogens.

6. Blueberries

Packed with antioxidants, brain-boosting B-6, B12, folic acid and phytoflavinoids, blueberries are also high in potassium and vitamin C, making them the top choice of doctors and nutritionists. Not only can they lower your risk of heart disease and cancer, they are also anti-inflammatory. Frozen blueberries are just as good as fresh. "Inflammation is a key driver of all chronic diseases, so blueberries have a host of benefits," advises Ann Kulze, MD, Charleston, South Carolina "I tell everyone to have a serving (a half cup) every day."

7. Dark chocolate or hot cocoa

New research has shown that dark chocolate is packed with antioxidants. Nutritionists recommend 60 percent or higher cocoa content; the darker, the better. The darker it is, the lower the fat and sugar content. Cocoa can also help prevent osteoporosis, especially as a way to introduce skim milk (rich in calcium and vitamin D) into the diet. After age 50, the recommendation is 1,200 milligrams of calcium daily to help prevent osteoporosis. One cup of milk provides 300 milligrams. Mounting evidence suggests that low levels of vitamin D increase death risk for seniors. A 2008 study found that death rates from any illness, especially cardiovascular disease, were higher in people with low vitamin D.

Cornell University food scientists report that cocoa teems with antioxidants that can lower cholesterol and help prevent cancer. When they compared the anti-cancer activity of cocoa to green tea and red wine-beverages known to contain antioxidants, they found that cocoa has nearly twice the antioxidants of red wine and up to three times those found in green tea. Hot cocoa is better than cold. When cocoa is heated, more antioxidants are released.

Why vitamin supplements are not to be taken lightly

With the importance of consuming the proper amount of vitamins and minerals, it's easy to assume that taking vitamin supplements would be a smart move, especially for seniors. This is partially correct. However, there's more to getting vitamins than just taking a pill. For most adults, eating a balanced diet that includes a rich assortment of vegetables, fruits, grains, nuts and other foods is enough—and the best way—to get all the nutrients a body needs.

The trouble is that as we age, changes in the lining of our stomach and intestines make it more difficult to absorb these nutrients. For this reason, introducing extra vitamins into your diet can compensate for these differences and improve health. How you get your extra vitamins and minerals is as important at the vitamins and minerals themselves.

Taking a vitamin pill with a glass of water in the morning is not enough. Many vitamins (including A, D, E and K) are not water-soluble; they're only digestible in fat. Taken on an empty stomach—or even with milk—many vitamins will simply pass through your system without any benefit. A study published in the American Journal of Clinical Nutrition found that cereal fortified with vitamin E has a very high rate of absorption into the bloodstream, whereas pills taken separately with the same food have inconsistent effects, and taking the supplements alone is largely useless.

"Applying vitamin E onto a grain cereal provided a huge and consistent increase in its bioavailability," said Scott Leonard, a Linus Pauling Institute researcher who conducted the study. "Even 30 international units (IU), the RDA for this vitamin, produced a large increase in new blood plasma levels (up to 500 percent compared to being taken alone or with milk)." According to Leonard, people who are taking vitamin supplements only with liquids on an empty stomach are getting few if any benefits from the supplements. Vitamins are absorbed better if they are part of or closely associated with the digestion of a food that has some fat in it.

Research published in the Journal of Clinical Hypertension shows that boosting levels of potassium in the diet may lower a person's risk of developing high blood pressure and may decrease blood pressure in people who already have "hypertension." Americans, for instance, consume less than half the recommended potassium they need, and researchers contend that low potassium intake contributes to the prevalence of high blood pressure in countries like the United States and Canada. Top natural sources of potassium include tomatoes, orange juice, bananas, white beans, dates, milk, raisins and potatoes.

Vitamin B12 has been making headlines, thanks to new research published in a 2008 issue of Neurology that suggests older individuals with low levels of vitamin B12 seem to be at increased risk of having brain atrophy or shrinkage. "We ought to be more aware of our B12 status, especially people who are vulnerable to B12 deficiency (including seniors and vegetarians)," said study co-author Anna Vogiatzoglou, a registered dietician at Oxford. "It's worth looking at your B12 levels. It's a simple blood test," advised Dr. Shari Midoneck, an internist at the Iris Cantor Women's Health Center in New York City.

There are some vitamins and supplements that seniors should avoid. For example, adult men and women after menopause don't need much iron. Too much iron can increase the risk of heart disease and cancer by counteracting the activity of antioxidants. It sounds like a marketing gimmick, but many "senior" or "silver" formula vitamin products are scientifically formulated to meet the needs of seniors and are almost always lower in iron and vitamin A and higher in vitamin B12. There is no standard "senior" formula, so you should always read the label of any multivitamin product. Remember—taking more than the RDA is not always better and can even be harmful.

You should also avoid taking vitamins in combination with some medications. Some medications can deplete or interfere with the absorption of certain vitamins, and some vitamins can interfere with the absorption or efficacy of medications. Results from research have also shown that taking stomach-acid blockers can contribute to a gradual lessening of absorption of B12 and other vitamins in the body. Always ask your doctor about what vitamins, supplements or foods should be take in combination with any medication.

Recommended vitamins for seniors

According to the National Institute of Aging, potentially beneficial nutrient supplements, particularly in the fight against Alzheimer's disease, include the following.

- Vitamin B12 (1,000 mcg per day)
- Folic acid (800 to 1,000 mcg per day)
- Vitamin E (400 to 800 IU per day)
- Vitamin C (1,000 mg three times per day)
- Coenzyme Q10 (50 mg three times per day)

Playing a part in a healthy diet

As we age, we need less energy—but we still need just as many of the nutrients in food. As a general guideline, seniors especially should enjoy a balanced variety of healthy foods, avoid foods with lots of calories but few nutrients and pick foods that are low in cholesterol and fat—especially trans fats and saturated fats. "Eating well is vital at any age, but as you get older, your daily food choices can make an important difference in your health," says Richard J. Hodes, MD, Director of the National Institute on Aging.

The amount of food you should eat depends on your age, your gender and your level of physical activity. According to the National Institutes on Health, as people get older, they require fewer calories than younger people. Women need fewer calories than men. The more physically active you are, the more calories you can consume without gaining weight.

The NIH suggests that a woman over age 50 should consume about 1,600 calories a day if her level of physical activity is low, 1,800 calories daily if she is moderately active and 2,000 to 2,200 calories daily if she has an active lifestyle. A man over age 50 should consume about 2,000 calories a day if his level of physical activity is low, 2,200 to 2,400 calories daily if he is moderately active and 2,400 to 2,800 calories daily if he has an active lifestyle. They recommend that a person with a 2,000 calorie per day intake should plan to eat a daily diet consisting of:

- 2 - 2 1/2 cups of fruit
- 2 - 2 1/2 cups of vegetables
- 7 to 8 ounces of grain foods (mostly whole grains)
- 2-3 cups of low-fat or fat-free milk, yogurt or other milk products

- 5 1/2 ounces of protein
- No more than the equivalent of 6 teaspoons of oil

"It is important for older adults to select foods that provide them with the nutrients and energy they need for healthy, active living," says Dr. Hodes. Enjoying a proper diet does more than help fend off disease and dementia. It improves a person's spirits. It provides the energy needed to remain active and strong. Moreover, it is essential to a person's quality of life.

A good meal can make a big difference at any age. Making sure you eat properly is one of the most pivotal things you can do to ensure your longevity. Liquid diets like Ensure™, canned meal replacements and nutritional drinks make very poor substitutes for real food. They may be suitable temporarily to supplement your diet if you are unable to tolerate solid food after surgery or illness, but they are not the answer to long-term nutrition.

Preparing healthy, appetizing meals is one of the most essential services a caregiver can provide for seniors who are too frail to cook for themselves. Misty Condon of Houston, Texas speaks of her 80 year old father, a former Navy pilot who was homebound after a series of minor strokes. "When he was by himself, he'd just lie in bed all day and never even eat," she says. That's when the family decided to hire a professional caregiver, Maria Vega, from Home Care Assistance. "But now with Maria helping him, once he is up and has had his lunch, he just keeps on going the rest of the day!" Ms. Condon reports that the simple act of eating lunch created a positive change in her father, giving him a reason to get up, get showered and get dressed. "Lunch was just what he needed to get him out of bed. Once he has eaten, it makes him so much more interactive and social," she adds. "Now he is able to go with Maria to the 'bark park' with his dog Sparky every afternoon, and he just keeps going and going."

With so much of our lives surrounding and depending on food, you owe it to yourself to get the food you need to do more than survive—but to enjoy living.

REMEMBER...

While seniors often need to eat less than they did when they were younger, the quality of the food they eat and its nutritional value are even more essential. Whether you cook for yourself or have meals prepared for you by a family or professional caregiver, make sure you are incorporating the 7 super foods and important vitamin supplements into your diet.

FOUR

Aging Well is No Accident

For seniors to live a full and natural life, it is crucial that they prevent falls and avoid accidents—by making the home as safe as possible. It is important to be aware that falls, fires and car accidents are the three leading causes of accidental injury and death among seniors. The good news is that most of these accidents are easily preventable, through awareness of safety measures, or through simple home improvements that make little or no impact on quality of life.

The myth of "accidental" falls

Each year more than one third of adults 65 and older suffer a serious fall. What makes this especially sobering is the fact that falls and fall-related injuries are a leading cause of death in older people—for seniors 85 and older, it's estimated that one in five falls results in death. According to research conducted by the Public Health Agency of Canada, 20 percent of injury-related deaths among seniors can be traced back to a fall.

In 2008, about 1.8 million seniors in the United States alone were treated in emergency departments for nonfatal injuries from falls, and more than 433,000 of these patients were hospitalized. Many of those who fall develop a fear of falling—even if they are not injured. This fear alone can cause seniors to modify their gait, limit their mobility and reduce their physical fitness—thereby actually increasing their risk of falling.

Until recently, most falls have been blamed on a single cause—precipitated by either a medical event or an "accident" related to the environment. Today, researchers know that falls are rarely the result of an isolated event. Rather, falls are complex events caused by the interaction of both internal and external factors.

Most falls represent the end result of a series of independent and often small risks. Individually, such risks pose no harm. Young people avoid many daily mishaps so naturally that they never even realize it. Eventually however, age, disability or compromised health can make it difficult to deal with even the simplest environmental risks. Often, a fall is ready to happen long before the victim encounters the event. So it is important to recognize and correct risky fall factors—both physiological and environmental —and break the chain of risk before a fall occurs.

Internal risk factors

A number of physiological and medical factors play a role in causing falls. Understanding them can help you reduce the risks they pose. Here are a few major ones.

- **Changes in muscles and bones.** As we get older, changes in muscles and joints not only make movement more difficult, but also make it harder to correct for a sudden loss of balance. Similarly, loss of strength in the legs or upper arms limits the ability to transfer in and out of bed or chair—increasing the risk of falling.

- **Vision changes.** As we get older it becomes harder for our eyes to adjust to varying levels of lightness and darkness. We also become more sensitive to glare. Decreased depth perception also makes it hard to distinguish high-contrast patterns from actual elevation changes. All of this means that it's much easier for us to trip and fall as we get older.

- **Balance problems.** Aging naturally diminishes the body's reflexes that enable people to properly interpret and re-orient their center of gravity as they move or walk. Changes in gait (such as walking with a narrower or wider stance than usual) increase the risk of catching a foot on an obstruction.

- **Cardiovascular difficulties.** Numbness in the limbs affects the ability to sense the ground; cardiovascular problems can also cause sudden loss of blood to the brain, resulting in fainting.

- **Neuropathy.** As much as 8 percent of the overall population and 20 percent of the senior population suffer from some form of neuropathy. Numbness of the feet and loss of balance are part and parcel of this disease. It is especially easy for seniors with neuropathy of the feet to slip on wet or icy surfaces.

- **Medications.** Many drugs (and their interactions) affect judgment and coordination. Tranquilizers can slow reflexes while other drugs increase the risk of fainting.

- **Chronic or acute diseases.** Falls may often be the initial symptom of a disease. Degenerative disorders only compound the risk of falls.

- **Depression, stress or lack of sleep.** Such issues can make seniors preoccupied and less alert to the dangers around them.

External risk factors

The environment (either indoors or outdoors) plays a major role in exposing seniors to falls. Falls in the bedroom, bathroom and dining areas are the most common, reflecting the amount of time spent in those areas. Relocation—such as moving between a home and a nursing facility, hospital or even a relative's home—can greatly increase the risk of falls, particularly by frail seniors. Lack of familiarity with floor surfaces and distance is only aggravated by a lack of expected visual clues for depth perception. Within these areas, here are some major items to consider and things you can do to limit the risk these environmental factors play.

- **Lighting.** Is there plenty of light in every room and along hallways and in stairways? Is there emergency lighting or a flashlight within easy reach?
- **Bathroom and kitchen.** Are there grab bars in the tub or shower and by the toilet? Are there non-slip bath strips or mats in the tub or shower? A bath bench and a raised toilet seat are valuable additions. In kitchens, countertops should be glare-free. Often-used items should be kept within easy reach.
- **Flooring.** Are all rugs (including bathroom rugs) tacked down or secured with nonskid pads? All carpeting should be low pile. Only no-wax cleaners should be used on floors—and shine should be eliminated as much as possible to reduce glare.
- **Stairways.** Hand rails are a necessity on both sides of stairways and outside steps. Care must be taken to ensure these hand rails are secure, so they do not wobble and

induce a loss of balance. Steps should also have non-skid treads. Marking the edge of the first and the last step with a color strip provides a helpful visual clue.

- **Furniture and living areas.** Arrange furniture so that walking paths are clear. Make sure all electrical cords are out of the way. Special care should be taken to ensure that the floor is kept free of all clutter.

What you can do to lessen the risks

While specific internal and external factors seldom cause falls all by themselves, the management, reduction or elimination of each risk will help prevent these factors from overlapping and causing a fall. Research results published in the British Medical Journal in January 2008 suggest that falls can be reduced by 50 percent when an individual's risks of falling are assessed and action taken to reduce them. Here are just a few ways you can reduce the risk of falling.

- **Engage in regular physical activity.** Helping seniors to remain physically active improves their balance, flexibility and strength, alleviates stress and depression, increases alertness and strengthens the heart and circulatory system. Even simple exercises such as stretching while in bed can improve the ability to stand, walk and even improve the reflexes needed to arrest impending falls. Seniors should be reminded to exercise regularly.
- **Have eyes checked by an eye doctor at least once a year.** Vision changes, as well as eye diseases like glaucoma and macular degeneration, can progress rapidly as people age, making it difficult for seniors to notice hazards when walking.

- **Manage a healthy diet.** While seniors tend to eat less than younger people, it's important not to skip meals. It's best to eat a wide variety of healthy foods. Limit alcohol consumption, too, since it can adversely affect alertness and coordination.
- **Monitor medications.** Use a log to keep track of all current medications. Learn their side effects, especially if they affect alertness or balance, as tranquilizers do. It's best to limit or avoid physical activities when under the effects of such medications.
- **Schedule regular checkups.** Even if a senior is feeling fine, it's important to have regular physical, vision and hearing exams. Eyeglasses and hearing aids should be worn as instructed and have the most up-to-date prescription.
- **Dress for success.** Safety starts with sturdy shoes. Nonskid soles, flat bottoms and good support are essential. Walking around in socks or smooth soled slippers can be dangerous. Sunglasses and a broad-brimmed hat are also helpful for reducing glare.
- **Use proper equipment.** A doctor, physical therapist or a medical equipment supplier can help you choose the best cane, walker or wheelchair. A power assisted seat-lift chair may be a wise furniture investment. You may also want to consider a personal emergency response device that can be self-activated, or hire a monitoring service that will call often and send help if no one responds.
- **Get the help you need to monitor safety.** An in-home caregiver can greatly help reduce the risk of falls. This is especially true for older people who have Alzheimer's disease or other dementia that makes them prone to wandering.

Be extra careful about seniors in institutions

As reported in the *Journal of the American Medical Association*, falls are more common in nursing homes than in the overall community. About 5 percent of adults 65 and older live in nursing homes, but nursing home residents account for about 20 percent of deaths from falls in this age group. Each year, a typical nursing home with 100 beds reports 100 to 200 falls and many falls go unreported. According to the *Annals of Internal Medicine*, as many as 3 out of 4 nursing home residents fall each year—that's twice the rate of falls for seniors living at home. The high ratio of residents to caregivers in nursing homes makes supervision much more difficult than the one-to-one attention an in-home caregiver can provide.

Seven hot tips for senior fire safety

Every year, more than 27 percent of all deaths by fire are to persons age 70 and over. According to the National Fire Protection Association, seniors are twice as likely to die in a fire when compared to the rest of the population. Adults over 85 have a risk that is four and half times that of the national average. "Seniors are vulnerable because they often live alone or are unable to respond quickly," says Ohio State Fire Marshal Michael P. Bell. "With education and planning, many of these fire deaths and injuries can be prevented."

The following suggestions are from the *Fire Safety Checklist for Older Consumers*, produced by the Consumer Product Safety Commission, the Association for the Advancement of Retired Persons (AARP) and the National Association of State Fire Marshals.

1. **Install smoke alarms and check them monthly.** At least one smoke alarm should be placed on every floor of the home. Many communities even have special programs that provide free smoke alarms to seniors, when available. Ideally, since many people prefer to sleep with their doors closed, separate smoke alarms should be placed inside bedrooms and in outside hallways. Place alarms either on the ceiling or 6-12 inches below the ceiling on the wall. Follow the manufacturer's directions for testing the alarm. Change batteries at least once a year.

2. **Be careful when cooking.** Pot handles should be turned inward when cooking on a stovetop. Cooking surfaces and surrounding areas should be kept free from clutter and grease build up. Use pot-holders and oven mitts. Avoid wearing loose clothing with flowing sleeves while cooking. Take a reminder with you if you must leave the kitchen with food cooking on the range top.

3. **Heat the home safely.** Have a professional inspect and service all heating equipment annually. Keep anything that can burn or melt far way from all furnaces, heaters, fireplaces and water heaters. Never use a stove or oven to heat the home.

4. **Use smoking materials safely.** Seniors should never smoke in bed, while drowsy or while under the influence of medication or alcohol. Ashtrays should be large and deep enough to hold smoking debris, and you should make sure the contents are cool before disposing of them in the trash. Better yet, consider kicking the habit altogether!

5. **Practice electrical safety**. Have a professional electrician inspect your home's wiring every ten years and make recommended repairs. Homes more than 40 years old are three times more likely to catch fire from electrical causes than home that are 11 to 20 years old because most older wiring was not designed for the capacity of today's appliances. Each appliance should be plugged directly into its own outlet.

6. **Keep matches and lighters away.** If seniors with dementia or children are present, store matches and lighters in a locked drawer or a high cabinet far out of reach. Make sure lighters include a safety mechanism.

7. **Know what to do in case of fire.** Know two ways out of every room in the home. Get out as soon as you discover a fire. Do not try to fight the fire or gather possessions. Once out of the house, dial 911 immediately, preferably from a neighbor's home.

It is important for everyone to know and practice these tips. Share this information with your family or conduct your own inspection to ensure the home is as safe as can be.

Risk factors that impair driving

Many of the changes that often come with age can adversely affect driving ability. These include:

- **Visual decline**—including poor depth perception, narrowed peripheral vision, poor judgment of speed and poor night vision, along with increased sensitivity to bright sunlight, headlights and glare.

- **Hearing loss**—especially the ability to hear important warning sounds while driving.
- **Limited mobility and decreased flexibility**—which increase response time, slow pedal selection and steering control and limit the ability to turn one's head to look for hazards
- Chronic conditions—such as rheumatoid arthritis, Parkinson's disease, sleep apnea, neuropathy, heart disease and diabetes can impair driving skills.
- **Medications**—since seniors often take more medications. Many combinations of drugs can impair judgment and slow response times.
- **Drowsiness**—is often due to medication side-effects or sleep difficulties that come with age, resulting in daytime tiredness and an increased tendency to doze off during the day (or while driving).
- **Dementia or brain impairment**—makes driving more dangerous and more frustrating. It can also cause delayed reactions and confusion on the road.

Warning signs to stay off the road

According to the National Institute on Aging, there are several critical indications that a senior may be losing the judgment or ability to drive.

- Incompetent driving at night, even if competent during the day.
- Drastically reduced peripheral vision, even if 20/20 with corrective lenses.

- Struggling to drive at high speed, even if he or she drives well at slow speeds.
- Erratic driving, such as abrupt lane changes, braking or acceleration, hitting curbs, missing turns or scaring pedestrians.
- Getting lost frequently, even while driving on familiar roads. Trouble reading street signs or navigating directions.
- Becoming frequently startled, claiming that cars or pedestrians seem to appear out of nowhere.
- At-fault accidents or more frequent near-crashes or dents and scrapes on the car or on fences, mailboxes, garage doors, curbs, etc.
- Failing to use turn signals or keeping them on without changing lanes.
- Drifting into other lanes or driving on the wrong side of the road.
- Range-of-motion issues, such as failing to look over the shoulder, trouble shifting gears or confusing gas and brake pedals.
- Increased traffic tickets or "warnings" by traffic or law enforcement officers.

When it's time to give up the keys

Realizing that you're no longer able to drive safely, or talking to a parent about his or her need to stop driving, is among the most difficult situations you may ever face. However, it's better if it comes voluntarily than by an order from a judge.

Living without driving is easier than you might think. It simply takes forethought to plan, schedule activities and combine multiple trips for a day when a relative or caregiver is available to do the driving. Often, seniors realize after a couple of weeks that their life is actually better not driving, and say, "Why didn't I do this before?" They may have been frightened and overwhelmed while driving, and find their new role as dedicated passenger to be a relief. Overall, many seniors are capable of driving safely, even into their eighties. But people age differently. Several factors place seniors at much greater risk for road accidents. More important, a person 70 or older who is involved in a car accident is more likely to be seriously hurt, more likely to require hospitalization and much more likely to die than a young person involved in the same crash. Knowing the risk factors and warning signs of seniors who can no longer safely operate a vehicle will help you gauge when it's time to give up driving or to take away the keys.

It's never safe to assume

Following the safety suggestions described in this chapter will go a long way in preventing more than 90 percent of the causes of accidental death typically suffered by seniors. Longevity depends on taking all reasonable precautions.

REMEMBER...

With proper attention, falls, fires and car accidents can be significantly reduced for all seniors. Use the checklists provided in the chapter to assess your level of risk in each of these areas. A professional caregiver can alleviate concerns around falling as well as provide convenient transportation services so that you can maintain your lifestyle even when you need assistance.

FIVE

The Psychology of Living to 102

Except when catastrophic injuries or illnesses are involved, psychological attitude can be the most important determinant in how long a person lives. This can be hard to believe, but it is definitely true.

Most of us guide our lives by a series of socio-cultural beliefs about dying that have very little actual basis in reality. These beliefs are typically accepted without much thought, and have often become destructive "truths" that are accepted by society without much question.

However, if we are going to live to 102 (or beyond), we can't just accept the common lore of death and dying. We need to look at these concepts and consider them openly – then decide about their truth and their value. Once we've given them some thought, we'll be able to see just how psychology can help us live long and live well.

We can divide this erroneous folklore into six different misconceptions about death. Let's take a closer look at each of these.

Misconception One...
- **Many seniors "want" to die. They have prepared themselves and "know" when their time is up.**
  Not true! Most seniors who "want to die" are suicidal and

suffering from depression. In fact, these seniors are similar to teenagers who "want to die". The only difference is that society accepts suicidal thinking among seniors and rejects it among teenagers. Any person who wants to die (regardless of age) needs treatment for suicidal ideation as a part of depression.

Misconception Two...
- **Seniors have had a "call from God" that it is time for them to die or "go and be with God."**
Imagine if your 11 year old child said such a thing! The sentiment is couched in religious terms, but it is really a depressed or suicidal thought.

Misconception Three...
- **Seniors die because they are "tired" of living.**
Being "tired" of living would not be accepted as a proper reason to die among people of other ages, and it should not be accepted as a normal statement from a senior. Rather it should be viewed as a sign of depression and the possible need for antidepressants. The assumption here is that the senior has been around a long time and is bored by the basic elements of life. In truth, we "get tired" because we have worn ourselves out physically from some act or group of acts. Most seniors, in fact, don't get tired from the process of living a long time.

Misconception Four...
- **People have a "time to die" and they die when that time comes.**
How does anyone know exactly what the correct time of death should be? There will be more than 1 million centenarians by the year 2050. Does that mean that all of us should live to be

at least 102 years of age? If we are in good health, should our "time" be 105 years. If we live to age 99, will we have died before our time? None of us know what the correct "time" for death is. In fact, the correct time is often the one you designate.

Misconception Five...
- **A senior is in so much pain, they are ready to die.**
  This is a conceivable scenario. However, in most cases, modern pain-killers do a good job of controlling pain. Wouldn't it be better to treat the pain rather than end a life? The exception here is the so-called "breakthrough" pain that occurs in some end stage diseases.

Misconception Six...
- **Major medical breakthroughs are needed for people to live much longer.**
  The fact is that any one individual can live longer or shorter regardless of what's going on in medicine. Yes, a cure for cancer or heart disease will increase the average lifespan, but it is not the only way to achieve this.

The Story of Bill

It is Bill's story that led to the decision to write this book. Bill was a feisty 97 year old retired musician. He'd had numerous serious illnesses, but he was a determined man. Despite his precarious health, he was confident about his ability to continue with his life. When we first met Bill he said that he planned to live long enough to celebrate his 102nd birthday. We all nodded and later agreed that he was just voicing the dreams of an old man. With his cancer, diabetes and colostomy bag, most people thought he should be happy if he lived to 98. For most people that would have been enough.

But not Bill! He wanted to have a real party for his 102nd birthday. He wanted a cake with 102 candles and he wanted all his many friends to be with him at this important celebration.

Bill got his wish. He lived to 102 years and had his party. There was a cake with 102 candles and nearly 50 friends who spanned the decades of his life – from his days in the symphony and as a teacher, to his later years when he was active around his neighborhood.

"I can't believe it has all gone by so fast," he said. "I can't believe my time is nearly gone, but it is a joy to see so many of the people who have made my life happy."

The night after his 102 birthday party, Bill died in his sleep – 23 hours past his actual birthday. Bill had specified the time and place of his death nearly 5 years in advance. And despite his advanced age and serious illness, he lived exactly as long as it took to celebrate his 102nd birthday.

Bill's friends were amazed at his longevity despite all his illnesses. But in many ways they were not surprised that his life ended as he had planned. Bill had always been a strong-willed guy who was used to doing things his way.

Stories like Bill's can be found from the beginning of recorded history. How many times have you read about someone who dies only after the family has been gathered around or when an impossible deed has been accomplished? Or about the grandparent who lived just long enough to see a beloved grandchild graduate from college? About terminally ill parents who, despite all odds, live to attend their child's wedding? And who can forget the story about Presidents Jefferson and Adams dying at the same time, but in different places?

We can control our life timetable

So why is Bill's story important to us? It is significant because it shows that we can have control over the time and place that we die. This is true in both the short-term and the long-term. Death does not have to just "happen" to us. Yes, we are bound to die some day, but we can often die on our own terms and in our own time frame (excluding accidents and acute illnesses).

Death doesn't just "sweep over us" and spirit us away. We can fight to survive acute conditions, we can postpone the act of dying and we can plan a life that is longer in time and richer in experiences than generations before us. Like Bill we can live to be 102, when others in the same circumstances would have died years earlier. And in the coming years there will be millions of us who make that choice.

Psychology teaches us to begin with a positive commitment

Almost every field of performance psychology starts with an effort to visualize and believe in a positive outcome. So, for example, if you want to win a race, you have to start by believing and by visualizing yourself winning the race. In sports, you need to visualize yourself making a basket, hitting a ball or sinking a putt. In living you need to visualize yourself living to a certain age, achieving specific accomplishments and overcoming certain difficulties.

Living to 102 years of age isn't all that different from winning a race. You have to start by visualizing yourself as alive, happy and well at 102. You need to really believe that you can do it. Then you need a plan to make your goal come true, and you need to follow that plan – day-in and day-out for the rest of your life.

Fortunately, you don't have to be on your own here. There are a number of discoveries in the field of psychology that can help develop a plan or roadmap that lets us live to 102 and beyond. With that in mind, let's review some of what psychologists have discovered about living a long life and see how we can use this information to live a longer, happier life.

The brain changes as you get older

No question about it! The brain shrinks by ten to fifteen percent over the course of a lifetime. And there is typically evidence of a decline in intelligence that goes along with this shrinkage. Often this decline has more to do with vocabulary and problem solving and less to do with a person's base of knowledge. (In fact, a sudden decline in problem solving ability and vocabulary has been associated with death).

The bad news about this is that if you do nothing, both your vocabulary and your ability to reason are likely to decline as you get older. The good news is that is possible to mitigate against these natural age-related declines in vocabulary and cognitive skill through regular mental exercise. And if you work at it, it is possible that you can even increase your thinking abilities.

Psychologists say that the loss of these skills is partially due to the fact that we lose interest in actively learning as we grow older. Many of us have a tendency to become more reactive or submissive in our approach to older life. We spend too much time sitting around passively listening to the radio or watching television, and not enough time doing something that involves the active use of our brain.

As the result of a variety of studies, psychologists have learned that regularly exercising the brain is effective in keeping our cognitive skills in peak condition. Further, they have discovered that peak levels of intellectual ability correlate positively to mental and physical well-being.

What this means is that seniors need to exercise the brain on a regular basis as they grow older. For example, they should read at least an hour a day in order to stay interested in the world and maintain a robust vocabulary. In addition, each day they should learn a new word and use it in conversation and writing. Seniors should not risk loss of vocabulary, no matter their age.

In addition to vocabulary, seniors should work on things like crossword puzzles or Sudoku to keep their mind fit. They should set aside one hour each day for this area of exercise. Finally, seniors should continue to use their brain (rather than a calculator) to solve everyday arithmetic problems. Add and subtract things in your head – and make sure that the problems you choose are something of a challenge. Even the healthiest human mind can become disoriented and slowly go blank without proper mental stimulation.

To live a long and happy life seniors need to keep their mind engaged. All seniors need to actively keep their mind from stagnating. If seniors exercise their brain each and every day of their life, they will minimize the loss of vocabulary and problem-solving ability associated with getting older.

It's bad enough that vocabulary and problem-solving skills erode with age; what's worse is that almost everyone's memory gets worse as well. Specifically short-term (rather than long-term) memory declines with age. Usually long-term memory stays about the same or gets better. Because of this discrepancy it is common for older people to dwell on the past and minimize the present.

Sometimes this can lead to social isolation. Older people tend to talk about what they can remember in the past, while younger people talk about the present. This often leads to a "disconnect" between seniors and the younger people around them. A frequent result is that the senior turns more and more inward, and has less and less chance to make use of short-term memory. And the greater the loss of current memory, the more there will be a tendency toward social isolation.

One thing is very clear. If seniors want to live a long time, they must be sure to consciously work on improving short-term memory.

Improving short-term memory

Here are just a few of the exercises a senior might consider doing on a daily basis in order to keep their short-term memory in the best possible shape:

- Spend a few moments each night recalling the events of the day. Pay particular attention to the date and the headlines in the news. Review a few conversations for content and ideas. Recall what you had for breakfast and lunch.
- Memorize phone numbers, names and word spellings.
- Visualize some of the scenes that you have witnessed during the day and recall the objects that made up that scene.
- Once or twice during every day, close your eyes and recreate a mental picture of what is 180 degrees behind you.
- Look at an object – then look away and draw a rough likeness of it.
- Memorize the first sentence heard each day.
- Keep in touch with what is current in movies, plays, books and music.

There is one final thing to consider when it comes to memory. Psychologists have found that seniors can improve their memory by using certain memory enhancing techniques. One of the most important of these is called "chunking". Chunking is a process by which a person "to-be-remembered" ideas or objects into meaningful groups. So for example, remember a specific phone number by first remembering the prefix and then the 4 digits connected with that prefix. This is far more effective than trying to remember a string of individual digits. Another common way of chunking is use the first letter of each "to be remembered object" and form it into an acronym. For example, if you wanted to remember that a kitchen contained a (t)urnip, (a)pple and (p)each, you would remember "tap" as your memory-jogging acronym. You should try one of these memory exercises at least once every day to keep your memory processing ability in shape.

Take five for the senses

Memory, vocabulary and problem solving abilities aren't the only things that decline as a function of getting older. Our senses decline as well. Vision, hearing, taste, smell and touch all decline in noticeable ways. The two most important senses, hearing and vision are a particular problem. The reason is straightforward: troubles with hearing and vision often cause seniors to withdraw from social relationships because they find it difficult to interact with others.

Loss of hearing, in particular, carries with it enormous social consequences. Often hearing-impaired seniors will actively avoid social situations and group gatherings because they find it so difficult to understand others and take part in ordinary conversations. Many times this isolation can lead to social withdrawal and depression – neither of which is conducive to an active, engaged life.

Failing vision is another matter. People who have trouble seeing don't read as much, directly affecting the amount of mental exercise that they are able to take part in. Just as with poor hearing, the vision impaired senior steps back from engaging with life, and this detracts from maintaining personal relationships.

It goes without saying that appropriate glasses and hearing aids are crucial for seniors who need them. These two items alone can make a huge difference in social and mental livelihood. The use of a hearing aid in particular makes many people feel old – or is seen as an admission of getting older. However, a hearing aid is a small step in avoiding the possible consequences of social withdrawal. It is, in short, a small physical sacrifice to make for improved social and psychological health.

Living to 102 doesn't mean that your body and your mind are in perfect shape when you get there. Rather it means that you are mentally and physically alive at 102 and doing the best with what you've got. Appropriate glasses and a hearing aid that works are minimum requirements for most people to have an enjoyable life in their later years.

REMEMBER...

Except when catastrophic injuries or illnesses are involved, psychological attitude can be the most important determinant in how long a person lives. If we are going to live to 102 (or beyond) like Bill, we can't just accept the common lore of death and dying. In living you need to visualize yourself living to a certain age, achieving specific accomplishments and overcoming certain difficulties. You also need to keep your mind engaged to stimulate short-term memory. Practice the suggested exercises to keep short-term memory in the best possible shape. And take advantage of any device that will help you remain socially and mentally engaged.

SIX

Help on the Home Front

You cannot even think about living to 102 without thinking about where you want to live. Numerous surveys have found that nine out of ten seniors would rather age in place, in their own home. Fortunately, the home care industry is already thriving. Hundreds of thousands of seniors who need non-medical, long-term care are getting the personal service they deserve, right in the comfort of their own homes, thanks to agencies like Home Care Assistance.

The shift to home care is quickly gaining ground as the primary option for senior care. In 2007, 43 percent of the $3.5 billion in benefits paid out to individuals through long-term insurance claims went to home care, while 33 percent went to assisted living and just 24 percent to skilled nursing care, according to the American Association for Long-Term Care Insurance.

Complications with senior facilities

Home care is especially attractive when considered along with the increasing problems reported in nursing homes. According to *The New York Times* (September 28, 2008), "94 percent of nursing homes were cited for violations of federal health and safety standards in 2007." Issued by Daniel R. Levinson of the Department of Health and Human Services, this report also noted that about 17 percent of nursing homes had deficiencies that caused "actual harm or immediate jeopardy" to patients.

Problems included infected bedsores, medication mix-ups, poor nutrition and abuse and neglect of patients.

Another concern is the risk for infection. Influenza virus and pneumonia are key risks among all seniors due to increased susceptibility with age. These risks increase when many people live in close proximity, especially when they have direct physical contact or even second-hand contact, such as when a single caregiver attends to multiple individuals, some of whom may be contagious.

Seniors are also more susceptible to antibiotic-resistant Staphylococcus Aureus (MRSA) virus, a dangerous, sometimes fatal disease for hospital patients and elderly residents. According to Christe Bruderlin-Nelson of the Health Behavior News Service, "MRSA spreads easily—most commonly via the hands of health care workers—and first-line antibiotics, like penicillin, are ineffective against the organism." As Bruderlin-Nelson notes, "Nursing home residents are particularly vulnerable because infection with the virus tends to increase with advancing age."

Furthermore, some elder care facilities have not benefited from much of the research that has gone into protecting hospitals from MRSA infections. This disparity was noted by The Cochrane Collaboration, an international organization that evaluates medical research, saying, "Nursing homes appear to have been short-changed in the medical literature on prevention, despite studies repeatedly reporting that residents are at higher risk." The reviewers add, "Many different ways of preventing the spread of MRSA have been studied, particularly in hospitals; however, we found no studies that looked at ways of preventing the spread of MRSA in nursing homes for older people."

Contagious urinary tract infections (UTI) are also disproportionately high in skilled nursing home (SNF) populations. According to Donald Kaye, MD, MACP, antibiotic-resistant UTI infections—without recognizable symptoms—have a prevalence of at least 10 percent in men and 30 percent in women in nursing homes. *The New England Journal of Medicine* reported that in one major survey, "Eight-five percent of patients with indwelling urinary catheters had asymptomatic bacteriuria; many were colonized with antibiotic-resistant bacteria." Even in cases where UTI symptoms exist, a study conducted at a state Veteran's Affairs nursing home found that the first-line antibiotic (ciprofloxacin) was only effective against about 40 percent of all urinary tract infections.

According to *The New England Journal of Medicine* "The high prevalence of infectious diseases and clustering of cases may reflect an increased susceptibility of patients in nursing homes to infections, high employee turnover or lack of attention to infection-control practices."
Fortunately, great steps have been taken recently to control the risk of contagious disease in elder care facilities. Vaccinations, extra screening of recently admitted residents, hand washing, high standards of cleaning and decontamination have proven effective in reducing the spread of disease. However, nothing can compare to the protection made possible by keeping a senior in his or her own home.

Eight home care advantages

In-home senior care offers many health and lifestyle benefits over facility-based care. Furthermore, home care that is provided by a reputable agency delivers additional advantages over family-based or independently hired caregivers. Here are a few reasons why agency-provided home care makes the best option for senior care.

1. **Nine out of ten seniors would rather live at home than anywhere else.** Senior citizens fear moving into a nursing home and losing their independence more than they fear death, according to a study reported in *The Wall Street Journal.*

2. **Families also prefer to have seniors remain at home.** Families know seniors would prefer to live at home and would like to honor that preference. Also, 82 percent of baby boomers fear their parents will be mistreated in a nursing home and 89 percent fear their parents will be sad.

3. **Staying at home is more comfortable.** Nothing beats the comfort of staying at home. This is true not only in comparison to a facility, but also compared to moving in with a family member. (Let's face it, any move is stressful!) On the lists of stress-inducing events, moving is third to death and divorce. Combine moving with the recent loss of a spouse, the onset of dementia or a growing disability—and even the simplest transition can feel traumatic.

4. **Home care is safer.** Institutionalized residents are at higher risk for falling as well as for developing acute illnesses such as pneumonia, dehydration, gastroenteritis and even antibiotic-resistant Staphylococcus infections. With a single caregiver attending to many people, it's harder to control cross contamination from one infected resident to another. The one-to-one personal attention by an in-home caregiver greatly lowers the risk of such illnesses. Hiring a caregiver from an agency also reduces the risk of infection by enabling a caregiver who is ill to call in sick, knowing his or her shift can be quickly covered with the help of the agency's staffing coordinator, without impacting the client.

Home care even eliminates many safety risks that come with moving into and walking around in new, unfamiliar places. Remember! Falls—which are often fatal to seniors—are twice as common in facilities than in private homes. Home caregivers can devote their constant attention to preventing falls, wandering, bedsores, kitchen injuries and other safety issues. A home caregiver can even call 911 within seconds of an emergency.

5. **Home care improves the quality of life.** By remaining in their home, with proper care, seniors are able to maintain the lifestyle and luxuries they are accustomed to enjoying. Keeping all their possessions and familiar surroundings, home care clients are able to visit the same stores, restaurants, neighbors and parks they already know. Plus, they can engage in the same activities they enjoy, rather than be expected to join in group activities with comparative strangers. In-home care enables seniors to savor their privacy and live their life as they choose, on their own schedule.

6. **Home care reduces stress and depression for the whole family.** A conservative estimate is that 20 percent of family caregivers suffer from depression, twice the rate of the general population. The role reversal of family caregiving is equally stressful on the relative giving and the one receiving care. Seniors especially remain keenly aware of the increasing physical and mental losses they are suffering. Plus, they may feel embarrassed that they require a family member (especially a child) to help them with certain issues such as using the bathroom. Hiring an agency caregiver

not only provides respite for the caregiving relative, it requires a minimal-impact change for the senior who needs the care.

7. **Agency-based home care is more dependable.** Turning to an agency to provide your home care is more reliable and safer, compared with hiring an independent caregiver. If your caregiver runs late or becomes ill or is unable to keep the scheduled visit, the agency will find a qualified substitute caregiver as soon as possible. With an independent caregiver, you're on your own. Agency caregivers are also more thoroughly screened and trained than independents. In addition to local and national criminal background and work authorization checks, Home Care Assistance also administers an exclusive psychological exam to verify honesty, kindness and conscientiousness. Their caregivers are also bonded and insured. Plus, the agency takes responsibility for scheduling, taxes and workers compensation.

8. **Home care prolongs independence and prevents institutionalization.** It doesn't take much in the form of a mobility limitation or health decline to render seniors unable to care for themselves. Simple personal tasks like bathing, using the toilet and cooking can become difficult ordeals. Fortunately, if they are assisted with these tasks, most seniors can lead fully productive and independent lives. The personal independence that home care provides seniors delivers huge benefits in physical and mental well being— and also benefits families and society as a whole.

Home care extends productive living

With the help of home care, many seniors are able to continue living productive lives even after debilitating illnesses or injuries. One example is Wesley Gilbreath, Sr., a once penniless hitchhiker who in 1964 parlayed $1500 he borrowed from a friend into what soon became (and still is) the largest outdoor advertising company in Houston, Texas. Just a few years ago, a severe stroke threatened to sideline Gilbreath forever.

The long-time millionaire, philanthropist, former politician and author of *The Road Out of Town is a 2 Way Street* became, for the first time, unable to fend for himself. That's when his family hired in-home caregivers from Home Care Assistance.

"They fix me good meals three times a day, clean-up, do the washing and do all the things I can no longer do myself. They even take me to appointments and shopping," says Gilbreath. "I'm a pointer man. I point and say 'I'd like one of those, one of those…and one of those!'"

When you're a businessman like Wes Gilbreath, pointing and getting isn't limited to store items. His stroke hasn't slowed down the way he conducts his business, including his investments in commercial real estate. The assistance and mobility provided by his caregivers enable Gilbreath to continue *growing* his business —not just reminiscing over it.

With the right assistance, people's abilities are boundless, regardless of their physical limitations. This concept is familiar to Rob Condon, the retired entrepreneur and U.S. Navy pilot referenced in an earlier chapter. Condon knows the importance of relying on others to go above and beyond what is humanly possible.

Beginning in 2006, when dementia threatened to strip Rob Condon of his independence, his family turned to a caregiver from Home Care Assistance. For six hours every other day, Condon's caregiver, Maria, helped him get out of bed, get showered, get dressed, get walking and get a nutritious lunch.

Recently, Condon suffered a massive stroke. Maria, his caregiver, even stayed with him in the hospital. Since coming home, Condon has required a caregiver to be present 24 hours a day, seven says a week. Maria drives him to speech therapy, too. "Home Care Assistance has been very responsive," adds Misty. "It makes us feel safe, knowing he's safe."

How an in-home caregiver can help

An in-home caregiver can provide help with any activities of daily living, including but certainly not limited to these essential tasks:

- Dressing and undressing
- Driving or using public transportation
- Shopping for groceries and clothing
- Preparing healthy, regular meals
- Taking a bath or shower
- Getting in and out of bed
- Engaging in social interaction and companionship
- Using the bathroom

- Doing laundry or light housekeeping
- Remaining active and interested in life and hobbies
- Walking, climbing stairs and getting around the house easily
- Medications reminders
- Assisting with prescribed physical therapy exercises

If you or a senior in your life needs help with any of the above activities, a home caregiver can make your life much easier.

In-home concierge services

Another advantage enjoyed by clients of in-home care agencies is the ability to have someone to turn to for assistance in obtaining a wide variety of services provided to seniors and their families. For example, if a pipe breaks in a senior's home, the caregiver or the caregiver's agency can help locate a reputable plumber. Whether it's as minor as making dinner reservations, as basic as needing help to call a handyman or as complex as seeking a financial or legal advisor, a home care agency can use its resources, experience and connections to assist seniors or their families in getting the help they need—even for tasks outside of the normal scope of caregiving.

While the agency might not have any cooperative referral arrangements in place with such professionals or service providers, the agency's staff can be very helpful in doing the research or making the call. This is especially true in matters closely related to the needs of seniors, such as finding a physical therapist, psychologist, professional geriatric care manager, fiduciary or senior trust officer, hospice provider or other senior-related services.

REMEMBER...

Staying at home with in-home care increases safety and comfort, reduces infection and depression and results in a longer, more independent life. 89 percent of seniors have a stated preference to live at home—compassionate and professional caregivers can help everyone achieve that wish with hourly or live-in care.

SEVEN

Get Active About a Longer, Happier Life

Let me very briefly summarize where we are at this point in the book. Living happily to 102 depends partly on chance and partly on choices or active decisions. But no matter what life cards you have been dealt, there are still many ways that you can personally make a positive difference in extending not only the number of years you live, but also the quality of those years.

One of the most important things seniors can do to extend and improve their lives is to exercise. This is true at any age and especially true for seniors. As seniors get older, exercise becomes even more important—because it is the only way to prevent the body's natural deterioration and maintain maximum strength, flexibility and function. *Sarcopenia* is what scientists call the loss of muscle, strength and quality of tissue often seen in older adults. Experts say that muscle mass declines about 4 percent each decade from age 25 to 50. The same deterioration occurs with bone density, especially in women after menopause. And get this! One in eight men over age 50 will have an osteoporosis-related fracture. The death rate in the year following a hip fracture is nearly twice as high for men as for women.

But there's some very important good news here. Loss of muscle strength, bone density, flexibility and balance isn't inevitable. According to the National Institute on Aging, "When seniors lose their ability to do things on their own, it doesn't happen just because they have aged. More likely it is because they have become inactive."

Even for seniors who have never been active, starting regular physical activity in later life can still greatly improve strength, endurance and flexibility. Even among frail and very old adults, exercise can improve mobility and functioning. Results of research have shown that people over 65, who exercise for at least 30 minutes three times per week, have the heart, lungs and muscles of a person ten years younger.

It's never too late to start getting active

No matter how old you are, exercise can improve the quality of your life. Best of all, improvements can be seen and felt rather quickly. Regular physical activity not only benefits the heart, but also helps prevent falls by strengthening bones and muscles. Plus, it slows Alzheimer's disease and other dementias by improving blood flow to the brain and reducing inflammation. Even reasonable amounts of walking can help control diabetes by improving metabolism. Plus, regular exercise has been shown to reduce stress and alleviate depression.

Despite these well-documented benefits, it can be difficult to motivate seniors to start and maintain regular physical activity. The fact is that a sustained exercise program doesn't require a gym membership, a personal trainer or any special equipment. It can be as easy as gardening or taking a walk around the block.

How exercise helps seniors avoid falls

Many seniors avoid exercising because they fear they'll injure themselves. Contrary to this belief, sensible exercise is one of the best ways to prevent injuries, especially from falls. Experts recommend strength training for older adults to help improve balance and decrease risk of falls.

We'll say it once again! Falls are the leading killer of seniors, with one in five falls resulting in death in seniors over 85. The National Athletic Trainers' Association and the American Academy of Orthopedic Surgeons say that exercise at any age, especially strength training, decreases the loss of bone density, keeps muscles strong and improves balance.

While younger seniors can usually catch themselves before an impending fall, older senior often have less strength and slower reaction times. Experts say certain exercises including yoga can help improve balance. Even seniors who are not interested in such activities can help improve balance by closing their eyes and trying to balance on one leg, walking heel to toe in a straight line or rising up and down on their toes while standing and holding onto a stable chair or countertop.

Good muscles make good bones

Strength training can reduce the risk of bone fractures and other injuries and even help seniors recover faster if injured. Currently only 13 percent of older seniors report engaging in strengthening exercises. Such exercises require muscles to work against a resisting force, such as gravity, weights or exercise bands. Examples of strength training activities include lifting weights or even resisting your own body weight by doing household or garden chores.

Anything that requires lifting, pulling, pushing, carrying or digging is a great activity for gaining strength. You can help strengthen your upper leg at the hip—a major site of osteoporosis—by bending properly using your legs for all the many times you need to lift things every day.

Although seniors may need longer periods of time to adapt to an exercise program, even frail adults can gain significant increases in strength and muscle mass through resistance and strength training. Strengthening exercises are especially important for older women. After age 35, women's bone density slowly decreases. This bone density drops sharply after menopause. Fortunately, weight-bearing exercise compensates for bone loss because exercise thickens bones as muscles pull on them.

One study of sedentary nursing home residents in their eighties showed that women who took part in mild exercises three times a week experienced an increase in bone mass of more than 4 percent. Residents who did not exercise experienced a decrease of bone density of 2.5 percent during the same period. No matter how much calcium you eat, including supplements, you will lose bone density unless you exercise. That's because calcium needs a reason to "stick" to your bones. Without exercise, all the calcium you eat is eliminated through urination. In fact, consuming large doses of calcium without exercising can even lead to the formation of kidney stones.

Keep on the weights to keep the weight off

Exercise will help you maintain your weight by slowing your metabolism. This can help you avoid developing diabetes and heart disease. Weight-bearing exercises also help you maintain or lose weight because muscle burns more calories than body fat. Every pound of muscle burns 6 calories per hour automatically, just on its own. Plus, increased circulation can help your digestive system stay healthy and keep your immune system strong.

The American Cancer Society says that physical activity can help protect against some cancers by balancing caloric intake with energy expenditure. Studies suggest that regular exercise can reduce the risk for cancer of the colon, rectum, prostate, endometrium and kidney. It may also help prevent breast cancer among postmenopausal women.

Brawn for brains: how exercise fights Alzheimer's disease

One surprising effect of exercise is its impact in reducing the development of Alzheimer's disease and other dementias. New research results based on MRI scans finds that exercise positively affects the brain's hippocampus region, an area that is important for both memory and balance. (The hippocampus is one of the first parts of the brain to suffer damage from Alzheimer's disease.) Exercise and increased physical fitness also slow down age-related brain-cell death in healthy older adults.

Researchers have found that patients who are more physically fit have less brain-tissue atrophy, while those who are rated as more sedentary have more brain damage. "We're able to locate the changes associated with fitness to the actual memory region, the hippocampus, which is a key area for Alzheimer's-related atrophy," said Robyn A. Honea, Ph.D., a lead investigator on the study. A September 2008 study in the *Journal of the American Medical Association* says a test of older seniors with memory problems who participated in a home-based physical activity program showed that they experienced improvement in cognitive function. The scientists suggest that delaying the onset of Alzheimer's disease by 12 months could prevent 9.2 million cases worldwide. This study was especially encouraging because the home-based exercise program that achieved the positive results was not stressful or highly exerting. (Most of the participants used simple walking.)

For 24 months, participants in the study were encouraged to perform at least 150 minutes of moderate-intensity physical activity per week. The most successfully followed activity was walking, which resulted in 142 minutes more physical activity per week. Cognitive function was assessed with the Alzheimer Disease Assessment Scale over 18 months. By study end, participants in the exercise group had better ADAS scores than those in a comparative group who only exercised 20 minutes per week.

The benefits of physical activity persisted for at least another 12 months after the intervention had discontinued. Unlike medication, which was found to have no significant effect on mild cognitive impairment, physical activity was shown to be successful. Furthermore, exercise has the advantage of additional health benefits.

Exercise helps treat depression

Exercise also provides many emotional benefits. Seniors who exercise more have more energy, and that alone can improve their mood and outlook on life. There's also a sense of accomplishment that comes from completing an exercise goal. Remaining fit improves a person's self image, too. Engaging in exercise in a public place, whether through partner activities or simply going for walks and engaging with other seniors, provides a social environment that can help alleviate loneliness.

A report by scientists at Duke University Medical Center says that moderate, regular exercise may be just as helpful in combating serious depression in older senior as anti-depressant medication.

Over a five-year period, Duke researchers studied elderly individuals who had been diagnosed as suffering from major depressive disorder (MDD). Participants were divided into three groups: one that exercised only, one that exercised and took antidepressant medication, and one that took the medication only, without exercise. The groups that exercised walked around a track for 30 minutes three times a week. None of them had been exercising previous to the study.

After 16 weeks, the scientists used psychiatric diagnostic tests to measure and rate the participants' symptoms of depression. These symptoms include depressed mood or loss of interest or pleasure combined with at least four of the following: sleep disturbances, weight loss, changes in appetite, psychomotor agitation, feelings of worthlessness or excessive guilt, impaired cognition or concentration and recurrent thoughts of death.

The results: 60.4 percent of the patients who only exercised were no longer depressed after 16 weeks, compared with 65.5 percent for the medication group and 68.8 percent of the combination group. The statistical similarity came as a surprise, said the scientists.

Exercise as a substitute for antidepressants

Dr. Joseph Gallo of the University of Pennsylvania in Philadelphia says that elderly patients often deny depressive symptoms. "Using exercise to treat those symptoms could be effective because exercise builds on self-efficacy and self-confidence." He also suggests that exercise might be beneficial because patients actually take an active role in trying to get better—compared to the very passive act of simply taking a pill.

"While we don't know why exercise confers such a benefit, this study shows that exercise should be considered as a credible form of treatment for these patients," says psychologist and study leader James Blumenthal.

Getting yourself into action

It is safe for most adults older than 65 years to exercise. Even patients with chronic illnesses such as heart disease, high blood pressure, diabetes and arthritis can exercise safely. In fact, many of these conditions are improved with exercise. However, before beginning any exercise routine, seniors should consult their physician.

If a new exercise program causes muscle soreness or joint pain the day after exercising, it's important to rest. The next time, exercise should be done at a lower intensity. If the pain or discomfort persists, talk to your doctor, especially if exercising causes any of the following symptoms:

- Chest pain or pressure
- Trouble breathing or excessive shortness of breath
- Light-headedness or dizziness
- Difficulty with balance
- Nausea

Women who have osteoporosis need to be aware that certain activities may increase their risk of fracture. According to *Everybody's Bones: A Handbook for the Prevention and Management of Osteoporosis*, exercises that may increase the risk of fracture include:

- Dynamic abdominal exercises, like sit ups
- Twisting movements, such as golf swings
- Trunk flexion, or bending forward
- Sudden jerking movements
- High impact exercise
- Jumping

It doesn't take much effort to reap big rewards

According to the American Cancer Society and the American College of Sports Medicine (ACSM), health-related benefits may be obtained from a surprisingly low level of aerobic exercise. "It is now clear that lower levels of physical activity...may reduce the risk for certain chronic degenerative diseases and improve metabolic fitness."

The ACSM prescribes that even seniors over 65 should engage in moderate aerobic exercise frequently—3 to 5 times per week —for a total of 20 to 60 minutes each day. However, the exercise can be accomplished in 10-minute increments accumulated throughout the day. According to the ACSM's guidelines, a well-rounded exercise program should include a combination of aerobic exercise, strength training (using weights) and flexibility training (using stretching). For those over age 65, such a program can improve muscle strength, reduce joint pain, improve range of motion, increase muscle flexibility and offset naturally occurring musculoskeletal changes that can significantly impair daily life.

Tips on becoming more physically active

If you're looking to get started, there are a few simple steps that will help you get going. Here are eighteen suggestions from the

International Council on Active Aging (ICAA), an association that supports professionals who develop wellness and fitness facilities and services for adults 65 and over.

1. **Get a checkup**. Meet with your healthcare provider to see if any health issues need to be considered before beginning an exercise program. Ask your health care provider about ways you can safely increase the amount of physical activity you already do now.

2. **Know your options**. Before starting any program, examine your options. Pick a program you know you will enjoy. Some individuals like to go to a gym and do a structured workout, while others enjoy a neighborhood-walking club. Either will help improve your fitness, ability to function and quality of life—but only if you do it regularly.

3. **Determine the best participation style**. Would you or your loved one prefer taking a class or going solo? What's better, morning or night? Is indoor fitness appealing, or does outside activity sound more fun? What's more realistic —dedicating large blocks of time to a physical activity (such as a weekend hike) or scheduling exercise in shorter, more frequent intervals?

4. **Start slowly**. Start lightly and build up to more intense activity. Many seniors are eager to get started and sometimes overdo it, which usually makes them sore and may cause them to stop exercising.

5. **Find an activity partner**. Many seniors find it helpful and motivating to find a friend to exercise with. Whether it's a

friend to walk with in your neighborhood or a personal trainer at a gym, that appointment makes doing the walk or workout more likely.

6. **Set specific short- and long-term goals**. Make goals as specific as possible. For example, a brisk, 10-minute walk in the morning before breakfast, at lunchtime and after dinner on Monday, Wednesday and Friday. Being specific helps make the activity a priority. Long-term goals are also important, such as working up to an activity that may feel too physically difficult at the moment, but may be accomplished with a little effort and practice.

7. **Create a support network**. Tell friends and family about new exercise goals and ask for their support and encouragement. Involving others often helps seniors keep commitments. Ask for telephone reminders and even invite participation from other seniors in the support network.

8. **List the benefits that can be expected from the exercise program**. Make sure these benefits are reasonable. Many seniors expect enormous benefits, such as losing 30 pounds in a month. When these benefits don't materialize, they feel disappointed. Be realistic when setting goals.

9. **Count every step**. Wear a step counter throughout the day to count how many steps you take. One study showed that pedometer users increase their physical activity by 26.9 percent. Less active seniors tend to take about 4,000 steps or fewer per day. Aim to do 250 to 1,000 additional steps of brisk walking, until you reach 8,000 to 10,000 steps in a day.

10. **Keep moving all the time**. Stretch, walk, march in place, stand and sit as many times as possible when you're talking on the phone or during television commercials.

11. **Consider joining a class**. Select an exercise class appropriate for your health status and ability. Check with your local YMCA or YWCA, senior center, city recreation program or health club to view the course offerings. Visit the local arthritis foundation for a list of all aquatic and land-based classes designed for those with arthritis conditions.

12. **Wear the right shoes**. Foot comfort and support is important for all impact physical activities. It is important to wear well-fitting, sturdy shoes. Your shoes should have good arch support and an elevated and cushioned heel to absorb shock. Even seniors who have arthritis, diabetes or orthopedic problems can remain physically active with the help of appropriate shoes.

13. **Drink plenty of water**. Hydration is important in reducing fatigue, staying cool and replenishing what is lost through perspiration.

14. **Guard against the sun**. Wear sunscreen, sunglasses and a hat for sun protection and to reduce glare that could cause a fall. Exposure to direct sunlight has also been found to cause or aggravate cataracts.

15. **If it hurts, don't do it**. Pain should be worked around, not through. Stop the activity if it causes pain, dizziness or shortness of breath.

16. **Warm up and cool down**. It's important to take time to warm up, cool down and stretch. This helps prevent injury and soreness to muscles and joints.

17. **Reward yourself**. Once you've reached your goal, treat yourself to something that reminds you of what a good job you've done and encourages you to continue. Make it something that feeds your spirit, but is not necessarily food or an expensive purchase.

18. **Don't quit**. Just like brushing your teeth, you can make exercise part of your daily life. Incorporating exercise as a permanent lifestyle change should be the ultimate goal.

The best fitness program for seniors is one that's easy to stick to

When choosing an exercise program, you need to examine your expectations (what results you want to achieve), your abilities (including any medical issues) and your motivation (what you will find most rewarding from exercise).

As has been noted, the best and most sustainable exercise program for seniors is walking. Walking is a great low-impact exercise. It's safe and effective for mobilizing previously inactive seniors. It's easily done almost anywhere and does not require any special equipment other than shoes. A comfortable, 30 minute a day walking routine is easy on the bones, muscles, heart and joints. It can be done at any time, with or without a companion. Plus, it can involve the added element of social interaction and inspiration from being outdoors in changing scenery. Best of all, getting started is as easy as placing one foot in front of the other.

For disabled or wheelchair-bound seniors, there are many exercise programs that involve seated exercises, including "Chairsercise" and "Sit and Be Fit" programs. These and similar exercise programs are available through DVD videos, the Internet and in books and are often offered through live classes at many senior centers. Also, these seniors may want to consider water-based activities.

Gardening is growing as a solution for senior exercise

If you like to work in your garden for thirty minutes a day, you may already be getting the exercise you need. At least during the warm months, many seniors find gardening to be a good way to keep their minds busy while benefiting from hours of activity. A new study by Kansas State University found that gardening builds bone density because it includes weight-bearing activity such as pushing a lawn mower, digging holes, pulling weeds, carrying soil and other tasks that require the use of large muscle groups in the body. However, gardening's value as exercise is limited by its seasonal nature, since seniors spend less time gardening or maintaining a yard in the winter than in the warm growing season.

Physical activity guidelines for seniors

Recently released recommendations from the Department of Health & Human Services specify key guidelines for the amount and types of exercise needed for seniors to remain healthy. "Regular physical exercise is essential for healthy aging," says the report. "Adults aged 65 and older gain substantial health benefits... especially important because this population is the least physically active of any age group."

Aerobic activity and muscle-strengthening activity are the traditional types of exercise recommended for all adults.

Key exercise guidelines for seniors

- Seniors should avoid inactivity. Some physical activity is better than none.
- Seniors should do at least 150 minutes a week of moderate-intensity or 75 minutes a week of vigorous-intensity aerobic physical activity, or an equivalent combination of moderate- and vigorous-intensity aerobic activity. Aerobic activity should be performed in episodes of at least 10 minutes, spread throughout the week.
- Seniors should also do muscle-strengthening activities that are moderate or high intensity and involve all major muscle groups on 2 or more days a week.
- Seniors should do exercises that maintain or improve balance if they are at risk of falling.
- Seniors should determine their level of effort for physical activity relative to their level of fitness.
- Seniors with chronic conditions should understand whether and how their conditions affect their ability to do regular physical activity safely.

When older adults cannot do 150 minutes of moderate-intensity aerobic activity a week because of chronic conditions, they should be as physically active as their abilities and conditions allow.

What makes the right exercise?

Walking the dog, gardening, pushing a lawn mower, doing yoga or tai chi, or taking a dance or exercise class—all types of aerobic activity count toward the guidelines. The guidelines encourage seniors to do a variety of activities, to make exercise more enjoyable and reduce the risk of overuse injury.

"Older adults should strongly consider walking as one good way to get aerobic activity," the guidelines say. Many studies show that walking has significant health benefits. It has a low risk of injury, it's easy to stick to and it can be done year-round and in many settings, indoors and out. If you're currently inactive, you should increase your amount of physical activity gradually over a few months and avoid vigorous aerobic activity.

REMEMBER...

No matter how old you are, exercise can improve the quality of your life. Best of all, improvements can be seen and felt rather quickly. Regular physical activity not only benefits the heart, but also helps prevent falls by strengthening bones and muscles. Plus, it slows Alzheimer's disease and other forms of dementia by improving blood flow to the brain and reducing inflammation. Regular exercise has also been shown to reduce stress and alleviate depression. You should only be as physically active as your abilities or conditions allow.

EIGHT
Getting Care That Goes Anywhere

Having a high quality of life while living happily to 102 includes not only the freedom to stay where you want—but also the freedom to go where you want. Whether you're at home, riding around the neighborhood or even traveling around the world, having assistance that's as mobile as you are is a necessity.

One of the unique advantages of in-home senior care is that it isn't limited to the home. Your caregiver can go wherever you go—to the store, to the great outdoors, to another city or beyond. The assistance of your personal caregiver can also be a lifesaver —literally—in the event you have a hospital stay. Also, should you eventually decide to move into an assisted living facility, you don't have to leave your personal caregiver behind. Think of your caregiver as your portable, personal life-preserving partner.

Travel companionship, care and safety

One of the deepest regrets many seniors report is their inability to travel far from home. The travel bug is hard to beat, whether you've enjoyed a lifetime of world travel and don't want those days to end, or never had the time to travel until you retired but are now in no physical condition to realize your dream of seeing other places. Maybe you would like to connect with relatives at a family reunion far from where you are. Or perhaps you would like to get together one more time with your band of brothers or sisters with whom you served during the war. Although seniors might think that travel plans are out of the question due to their personal needs, a caregiver can be the ticket to making such a trip.

"After thirty years watching Masterpiece Theater on public television, I wasn't about to let my minor stroke keep me from seeing England for the first time," said Peggy Shoemaker of Los Altos, California. "There was no way I could do it alone, but I knew this might be my last chance to take such a trip," she said. "Having a caregiver with me gave me the mobility, clear thinking and camaraderie I needed. We had a wonderful time," she laughs. "And everyone thought I must have been famous—because I brought my own 'valet' with me!"

Making hospitals stays more hospitable

One of the most critical places to have a caregiver is during a hospital stay. Many people find this a surprising concept. You would think that having nurses, doctors and medical staff so close by would make hospitals one of the safest places to be. Sadly, this isn't the case. With one or two busy nurses working 12-hour shifts and handling many patients with critical needs, it can be a long wait from the time a patient pushes a call button to the time a nurse checks in.

The gravity of these risks is no surprise to hospitals, where falls are among the most common occurrences reported. The prospects of injury and financial burdens due to patient falls are among the most serious risk management issues faced by hospitals today. Ten percent of fatal falls for seniors occur in hospitals. Even minor falls can lead to fracture, soft tissue or head injury, fear of falling, anxicty or depression.

Over the last few years, hospitals throughout the United States and Canada began adopting patient safety goals, which task them to reduce the risk of patient harm resulting from falls. Now hospitals assess and periodically reassess each patient's risk for falling and take action to address any identified risks.

Dementia, disorientation and medication are the leading causes of falls in hospitals. Only about 14 percent of all falls in hospitals are due to accidents. The remaining falls are actually anticipated physiological events. Short of restraining patients to their beds, hospitals are left with few options to protect their patients. Hospital sitters are the most effective solution.

Hospital sitters—your 24/7 guardians

The best safety precaution while in a hospital is a specialized caregiver known as a sitter. Hospital sitters provide round-the-clock companionship and record observations of any problems the patient may be having. Sitters monitor and keep the patient company, converse and read or even run errands for the patient. However, sitters cannot aid or participate in any patient care or physical contact and must stay out of the way of hospital staff. When sitters are used, they are under the direction of the registered nurse on the ward.

In the event of an urgent patient need, a fall or a medical emergency, the sitter will be there to immediately summon the nurse in charge. Often hospital administrators are so concerned about common safety risks that they hire hospital sitters directly to watch over patients.

Hospital sitters warm hearts, not just seats

While safety is critically important, hospital sitters do more than help prevent falls and alert nurses to medical emergencies. "Raw companionship is great medicine," says Dr. Mynra Lee, a physician at Mt. Zion Medical Center. "Despite so many busy people running around, hospitals are lonely places," she says. "I see a remarkable difference in the recovery and responsiveness of patients who have the company of another person watching over them, even if they are unable to converse together."

Knowing another person is in the room watching over them—especially if it's someone familiar like a regular caregiver, makes patients feel more secure and makes a hospital room safer. This positive presence may even improve care from nurses and other hospital staff. Debbie Meyers, a registered nurse, admits that patients who have a visitor or sitter in their room often receive more attentive care. Says Meyers, "A hospital sitter can lead nurses to respond more quickly to the patient because they have an audience."

Although hospital sitters can't take an active role in caring for the patient, they can do a lot more than just sit there. One of the most helpful tasks that sitters can do is to keep a journal. Sitters can record every doctor visit/outcome that occurs during their shift, describe any procedures done and the expected and actual outcomes, note observations of the patient during their shift, list any questions they have for medical personnel or for the patient's family. Sitters can also maintain emergency contact information for the patient's family or advocates, as well as essential legal documents—including a copy of the Durable Medical Power of Attorney and Living Will (Advanced Directives), in case a relative is unable to be contacted for a critical decision.

Hospital sitters provide peace of mind for the patient's family. They supply vigilance that ensures safety and companionship and reduces a patient's boredom and depression. They also enable the patient's family to go home and rest, knowing their family member won't be alone.

A faster road to rehabilitation

Exercise is essential for strength, safety and health. This is especially true for people who are recovering from an injury or stroke or from surgery involving a joint, bone or muscle. If you're hospitalized for anything—even something that doesn't affect your movement—you may lose strength and mobility from lying in bed. You may require time in a rehabilitation center before or after returning home. If so, a caregiver can be a great partner in your recovery.

One basic but important way a caregiver can help in this situation is by providing transportation. Doctor's orders commonly prohibit discharged patients from driving a car or lifting anything heavier than a few pounds for a couple of weeks after major surgery. A caregiver can improve your life during your recovery by handling tasks you used to take for granted, like doing laundry or shopping for groceries. Your caregiver can even keep you from feeling housebound while you recuperate by enabling you to get out and visit friends or attend services where you worship. Most important, a caregiver will drive you to appointments with your physical therapist, as well as any follow-up appointments with your doctors.

The biggest advantage a caregiver offers after hospitalization is moral and physical support with prescribed rehabilitation exercises. One secret to the success of champion athletes and bodybuilders is that they work out with a personal trainer or a partner. An exercise partner not only "spots" you (protecting you from injuring yourself if you falter or fail during an exercise), but also offers continuous encouragement and safely pushes you beyond what you thought possible. That's how you build strength, by gradually and safely pushing your limits. Like a personal trainer or exercise partner, your caregiver will be there to motivate you and cheer you on while continually watching out for your safety. Without such motivation and assistance, many people might not complete or even begin the exercises prescribed by their physical therapist.

Daily or more frequent physical therapy exercises are essential in the days and weeks following a hospital stay or stroke. Such activities not only help stroke survivors in recovery or retraining of sensory-motor skills, strength, endurance and function, studies show a beneficial impact of such exercises on preventing future strokes or various cardiovascular events. It is traditionally believed that most if not all recovery of motor function occurs during the physical rehabilitation of individuals within several months after stroke.

"Unfortunately, failure to follow rehab exercises is a major reason stroke remains a leading cause of long-term disability," says Neil F. Gordon, MD of the American Heart Association. "Consequently, stroke survivors are often de-conditioned and predisposed to a sedentary lifestyle that limits performance of activities of daily living, increases the risk for falls and may contribute to a heightened risk for recurrent stroke and cardiovascular disease."

The emotional support and social interaction that a caregiver provides can have a significantly positive effect on long-term recovery from stroke. Studies have shown that even in stroke survivors who experience good physical recovery initially, social isolation still poses problems for continued success. Many stroke survivors don't have the equipment in their home to sustain interest in an exercise program over the long term. They will need to seek assistance, equipment and facilities in the community. Having a caregiver to drive you to the physical therapy office or gym can solve this problem.

Because of mobility difficulty and self-consciousness over compromised physical or mental abilities, many stroke survivors become socially withdrawn or depressed. The incidence of post-stroke depression ranges from 18 percent to 68 percent. By bringing emotional support, motivation, transportation, companionship and enabling greater interaction with the outside world, caregivers assist in rehabilitation far beyond the physical realm.

After suffering a severe, right hemorrhagic stroke, Lucy Granger enlisted the help of a Home Care Assistance caregiver, Tania Santos. Tania stayed every day between 8 in the morning and 4 in the afternoon. In addition to cooking, driving and housekeeping, Tania assisted Mrs. Granger with her essential physical therapy exercises, three times a day—right in the comfort of home. "Tania didn't just drive me to my physical therapist appointments," says Mrs. Granger. "She actually trained with the physical therapist so we could do the exercises together on our own." Having a caregiver helped Mrs. Granger combine physical therapy with fun socialization. "We still go shopping quite a bit," she says. "We like to walk around the neighborhood and talk to neighbors. That's part of my physical therapy, too!"

Tania's help has meant more than an increase in strength and mobility. It has ensured that Mrs. Granger has not had to retire from life. Succeeding at her arduous short-term physical therapy goal propelled her toward her long-term goal of becoming a volunteer tutor for at-risk high school students. "I hope to devote the rest of my life to serving others," says Mrs. Granger. "A little thing like a stroke isn't going to stop me."

How to feel more at home even when you don't live at home

Although assisted living facilities (ALF) and other institutions do have a high ratio of residents to caregivers—usually one caregiver for up to a dozen seniors—that doesn't mean you have to give up the personal attention you deserve. You can bring your own private caregiver into the facility.

"The house had just become to big for me and it was becoming harder to get around, since all the bedrooms were upstairs," said 85 year-old Gretchen Fischer. "Assisted living made sense, but I didn't want to just be one of the crowd." So Mrs. Fischer hired her own private duty caregiver to attend to her for a few hours every day.

Large numbers of residents in assisted living centers also have personal caregivers. Caregivers provide services that some assisted living centers are unable to provide, such as one-to-one help, companionship, support getting in and out of bed, bathing assistance and nighttime bathroom trips.

"I have to go the bathroom several times a night but it's hard for me to get out of bed on my own," said Greg Pescobal. "I couldn't be in some place pulling a cord and waiting for someone on the nursing staff to come in and help me. I'd never make it!" Mr. Pescobal found relief through a personal caregiver who sits overnight in one of the rooms of his apartment at the ALF. "It's such a simple thing, yet having the help I need to get up at night when I want, without resorting to sleeping in adult diapers, makes me feel a lot more human."

A private caregiver at an ALF might seem like a luxurious expense to some, but if you're used to living a certain independent lifestyle, there's no reason why you shouldn't expect to enjoy the same advantages and luxuries even in your later years. Family members of residents with Alzheimer's or some other form of dementia might also consider hiring a private duty caregiver. The risk of falls and self-injury is much higher in facilities and nursing homes. There just aren't enough staff member eyes to provide the level of safety monitoring that some seniors need. "Every time I visited my aunt in the nursing home, I would see bruises or her glasses would be broken or her wrist would be sore," said Mary McGregor. "It turns out she'd been falling all the time, when no one was around! That's when I knew she couldn't go on without someone watching her 24 hours a day."

One might think that ALFs would be reluctant to allow private caregivers to work in their facility. In reality, private caregivers are not seen as competitors but as cooperators. Like many agencies, Home Care Assistance has positive relationships with assisted living centers. Facilities often turn to agencies for caregivers if they are understaffed, especially on weekends and holidays. "I actually encourage our residents to hire private caregivers to augment the service they receive," says the owner of one ALF in Boston, Massachusetts. "It not only relieves some of the workload of our staff, but anything that improves the quality of life and the satisfaction of our residents makes our facility look good, too. If our residents are happy, we're happy. They may even refer their friends to us as well, so everybody wins."

Perhaps the most important effect that private caregivers can have on residents of an ALF is enabling seniors to avoid moving to a skilled nursing facility. Caregivers provide attention, compassion and assistance that will slow physical and mental decline. As seniors become more frail, or their dementia becomes more advanced, their requirements exceed the regular care that an ALF staff can provide. Once that happens, the resident is usually moved into a skilled nursing facility. Every year, month or even day you can delay this transition, the better. Hiring a private caregiver to complement ALF care can extend life and happiness by many months or even years.

REMEMBER...

Home care can go anywhere! Whether you are in the hospital for a short stay or in an assisted living facility for the long run, a caregiver can help to provide the one-to-one attention and round the clock monitoring you need. For a faster road to rehabilitation and the peace of mind of constant care, consider a hospital sitter next time you check in for any type of procedure. In a facility, caregivers will enable you to avoid moving to skilled nursing! Whether at home or in another setting, caregivers can provide the care and companionship seniors need to slow physical and mental decline.

NINE
Giving Aging the Technological Edge

D ietary, medical and psychological advances are not the only
things that are pushing a happy life expectancy over the
three-digit mark. In the digital age, high-tech tools are making it
possible for seniors to live independently longer than ever before.
Home computers and cell phones are the backbone of a
transition from hospital-based to home-based health monitoring.
Other high-tech gadgets —such as motion detectors and sensors
to regulate temperature, lights and appliances—are helping
families and caregivers keep seniors safer and more comfortable.
Caregivers from agencies like Home Care Assistance even check
in and out of their live-in or hourly shifts using an innovative
telephony system, eliminating any doubts about the accuracy of
the hours worked.

You need only to browse the web to find companies specializing
in assistive technology. In 2008, the European Union committed
$1.5 billion to developing independent living technologies. Intel
partnered with Ireland's government to form the TRIL Centre
(Technology Research for Independent Living) to apply technology
to help the aged in fall prevention, cognitive function and social
connection. The National Institute on Aging is providing grants
to companies developing video-based systems to analyze senior
activity levels in the home. The Oregon Center for Aging and
Technology runs a living laboratory with hundreds of elder
volunteers, using computer games and sensors in carpets, walls
and appliances to detect cognitive decline and changes in gait.

And in May 2009, General Electric and Intel announced an alliance to develop and sell technology to help care for the elderly and chronically ill in their homes

The recent prevalence of these companies, monitoring systems and assistive technology is a response to the upcoming explosion in the senior population at a time when there will be fewer family caregivers. These devices may also make the job of caregivers easier and more effective, further delaying or altogether preventing the need for institutionalization of the seniors who depend on them. In a 2008 AARP study, 80 percent of family caregivers said that technology could make them feel that the person they care for is safer.

Technically speaking for home-based health

Health information technology is steadily reducing the need for many routine visits to the doctor. Even something as simple as a cell phone can be programmed to remind a senior to take diabetes medication. Other devices can check blood sugar and monitor blood pressure almost automatically. The results can then be transmitted to a doctor who can monitor any changes, make recommendations and be alerted in case there is a need for immediate medical intervention. It is estimated that by 2012, more than 3.4 million seniors in the United States alone will be using networked sensor applications to monitor and improve their health.

We are seeing major innovations for monitoring health remotely from the comfort of home. These include electrodes for monitoring brain activity, sensors for monitoring blood glucose and oxygen levels, respiratory rate, body temperature and physical activity. Because new sensor technologies are making these devices lighter, smarter and more reliable, they're perfect for use in home-based medical applications.

Blood glucose sensors are being developed that can even be implanted under the skin during a short outpatient procedure. Designed to automatically measure interstitial glucose every few minutes, without any user intervention, these sensor implants will send a wireless signal to a small external reader that monitors glucose levels continuously or on demand. By tracking the rate of change of glucose levels, the device can warn the user or caregiver of impending hypo- or hyperglycemia. In tandem with insulin delivery implants, such systems will be able to provide virtually automatic maintenance of optimum glucose levels. This will allow diabetics without the ability to test or manage their disease themselves the ability to live independently.

High tech in the kitchen and the bathroom

Appliances themselves are becoming aids to seniors living independently. The ipot, from Zojirushi Corp., is a popular kitchenware item in Japan. This electric kettle uses a radio transmitter to automatically send an e-mail twice a day to relatives to let them know if Grandma has made tea. Other kitchen appliances made especially for seniors automatically shut off if they detect inattention for a determined period of time.

Modern advancements in electric toothbrushes, with highly-effective vibrating or rotating bristles, make it much easer for a caregiver to effectively brush a senior's teeth. This is especially important for seniors with dementia, who need special attention when it comes to oral health because they are more susceptible to tooth decay and gingivitis, risk factors linked to Alzheimer's.

Getting a sense for fall prevention

Because falls are the number one risk for people of advanced age, fall prevention is the leading focus of a number of these emerging technologies. Fall prevention technology aims to develop algorithms that can help predict falls, plan safer routes, provide early warning of a senior's instability, deliver instant feedback and even improve intervention.

Personal emergency response systems have been used for decades to help seniors who have fallen and are unable to get up. Worn on a pendant, a battery-operated miniature transmitter sends a digital coded wireless signal to its companion receiver when a button is pressed, activating a telephone-based alarm system monitored by operators.

Wandering detection and telecare

Passive monitoring technology, also known as telecare, uses strategically placed activity sensors to establish a pattern of an individual's normal habits for sleeping, waking, bathroom use and overall activity. When the sensors detect a meaningful deviation from the person's normal activity, an alert is sent to a family member, caregiver or facility staff. Should it detect any emergency situation, it immediately sends a red alert via cell phone or pager. One advantage of this passive system is that it provides monitoring and summons help without the senior having to do or wear anything.

Other types of telecare systems being put in place for seniors include thermometers (for monitoring those at risk of hypothermia or heat stroke) and flooding and unlit gas sensors (for people with dementia). When the system triggers an alert, it sends an alert to a family member, caregiver or operator at a monitoring center who can then make the appropriate response. Thermometers and gas detectors can even be wired into the home to automatically adjust climate controls or shut off the gas and report what happened. In the case of people with dementia, they can activate a voice message to remind them to turn off the gas.

There are also many low-tech devices that alert caregivers to wandering. These include seat belt alarms (for use by mobility-challenged people with Alzheimer's disease or cognitive disabilities) that ring if the seat belt is disconnected. Plus, there are wanderer detection systems that use a miniature transmitter—worn as a tag, bracelet or pendant—that activates an alarm in a caregiver's receiver. And there are mattress sensors that are designed to alert caregivers if an individual with balance problems, Alzheimer's or other disability tries to get out of bed unattended.

Domo arigato, Mr. Roboto

Some companies are taking assistive technology even further into the future—with robots. Mitsubishi Heavy Industries has created Wakamaru, a domestic robot primarily intended to provide companionship to elderly and disabled people. Selling for about $14,000, the two-armed robot is yellow, 3 feet tall and weighs 66 pounds. Its mouth and eyes will change expression depending on the emotions of the person in contact with the robot.

According to its inventors, "Wakamaru can recognize the faces of people that have been recorded, respond when spoken to, meet a person's gaze, offer subjects of conversation, all to ensure naturally rich communication."

Wakamaru is just one of a number of robots developed around the world for use in senior care applications. Standard functions of these robots include reminding the user to take medicine on time and calling for help if it suspects something is wrong. For example, Sanyo created Hopis, a furry pink dog-like robot capable of monitoring blood sugar, blood pressure and body temperature.

An American-made device developed by scientists at the University of Massachusetts Amherst, uBOT-5, reminds owners to take medication, helps with grocery shopping and monitors the home environment for signs of trouble, such as a person falling down, calling 911 if necessary. It can also connect seniors with their families using a video Internet link.

Ifbot is the resident robot at several Japanese nursing homes. It can converse, sing, express emotions and give trivia quizzes to seniors to help with their mental agility. In 2008, the University of Tokyo unveiled a prototype eldercare robot called Mamoru ("to protect") that reminds users with dementia when to eat and take their medicine and uses a wide-angle camera and image-recognition software to find the location of various household items they may have misplaced.

The Norwegian government is currently examining robot eldercare as an answer to the anticipated shortage of senior care workers by 2020. "Robots will be the ones that are doing simple housework chores like washing clothes, dishes and cleaning the floor," says Olav Ulleren, head of a municipal group studying the concept. "Devices should be able to give daily medical tests, provide companionship and observation of the elderly and help with personal hygiene." It is hoped that using robots will enable senior citizens to live in their own homes longer and in comfort. "Rather than replace live caregivers," Ulleren says, "using technology for household chores would make human health care more personal."

High tech games for delaying dementia

Cognitive ability declines less in those who engage more frequently in brain stimulating activities. Cognitive training programs can actually reverse cognitive impairment in many seniors. Scientists are using their brains to come up with new ways for seniors to exercise their brains. Interestingly, some of the oldest electronic games are proving to be effective at helping seniors sharpen their memory and cognitive skills.

One such game is Simon® (now sold by Hasbro, Inc.). Simon is an electronic game of rhythm and memory skill invented in the 1970s that became a pop culture icon in the 1980s and is still selling today. With its four large color buttons, red, blue, green and yellow, the unit's computer chip lights these buttons in a random, successively longer sequence, playing a tone for each button. To win, the player must press the buttons in the same sequence. The longer it's played the faster the game goes. Researchers are finding this is a great game for improving short-term memory, even in people who suffer from dementia.

As computers become more popular with the elderly, more computer-based games and memory-building activities will be a key factor in improving the cognitive health, communication and even the enjoyment of seniors. Computer-based memory exercise programs are available for free online play through websites such as through http://www.thirdage.com/games or http://games.aarp.org. You can also try and buy computer games specially designed for seniors to help prevent or slow cognitive decline, available from websites including http://www.happyneuron.com and http://www.positscience.com. Already more than 23 percent of older adults in North America aged 65 and older play computer games, according to a 2008 survey. Seniors who do play computer games tend to play them more frequently than younger adults. Over one-third (36 percent) of seniors 65 and older say they play games everyday or almost everyday, compared with 20 percent of adults in other age groups.

Games don't have to be electronic. Activities that keep players actively searching for words (such as Scrammble®, Scrabble® and Crosswords) are especially helpful for improving word recognition and vocabulary retention, reducing memory loss. An observational study of people aged 75 to 85 who engaged in cognitive exercises such as playing board games, reading and doing crossword or Sudoku puzzles demonstrated a significant reduction in the likelihood of developing dementia over a five-year period than those who did not.

Brain Fitness Centers

Now there are even cognitive fitness centers that are available to seniors. Thousands of adults are visiting these "brain gyms".

Vibrant Brains in San Francisco, California is one such business. It has been open since late 2007 and has several hundred members who pay $60 a month to work out on 20 computer stations loaded with "mental fitness" software. Sessions are spent doing things like mental-fitness assessments and basic cognitive training. The Vibrant Brains "gym" has members who are seniors and want brain-fitness workouts to postpone or prevent dementia.

REMEMBER...

Technology is allowing seniors to stay more connected than ever before. When independent living is in the balance, something as simple as spending time doing brain exercises on the Internet or in a local brain fitness center can make all the difference. As telecare and other assistive technologies become available and accessible, consider how they can be used either separately or in conjunction with home care to offer the best senior care solution.

TEN
Other Secrets to Happy Aging

By now it should be clear that we have a surprising amount of power to extend the length and quality of life. Eating healthily, staying active, getting plenty of sleep and continuing mental exercise for your brain are key components to aging successfully. However, there are some other lesser known things that can be done to fine-tune the quality of life into later years.

Get social for a longer, happy life

One of the most important human needs is friendship and interaction with others. Humans share a basic, perhaps even biological, need for social connectedness and a sense of belonging. This is especially true for seniors, who have built a lifetime of relationships with friends, family, coworkers, fraternal societies, fellow veterans and others. Research shows that people who remain surrounded by a strong network of friends and social relationships into their later years are far more likely to age healthily and happily. Most recently in the May 21, 2009 issue of *The New York Times*, the cited research from the 90+ Study indicated that a combination of mental stimulation and social interaction through activities such as playing Bridge was even more effective in preventing or slowing down progression of dementia than the mental stimulation by itself.

One essential part of successful aging is that "being independent" doesn't translate into "being alone." What happens if a senior becomes unable to drive to social gatherings or connect with friends who share similar interests and life experiences?

Maintaining social connections is easy if there is someone to encourage interaction with friends, and someone to help with transportation. If there isn't a friend or family member who is able to help you keep up with social events, a private caregiver can greatly improve life by driving you to social activities at senior centers, book clubs, veterans hall events and more. Having someone who can serve as "social coordinator" and driver opens up a whole world of interaction opportunities, including:

- Driving to visit friends at restaurants or where they live
- Going out with the dog for a walk at public parks
- Participating in arts and crafts with others, such as sewing circles
- Joining bridge clubs, reading groups or other regular gatherings
- Taking adult education classes at the local college
- Inviting friends home—and providing transportation for them
- Attending worship services
- Planning group outings, field trips to local tourist attractions and even cruises or vacations
- Attending a local performance or sporting event, such as high school or college plays, concerts or sports outings
- Taking trips to the salon to have hair and nails done
- Becoming involved in political campaigns or social causes
- Volunteering for service organizations that can benefit from a senior's experience and advice

Staying socially active is as essential to healthy, happy aging as staying physically active. Left alone, it's easy for seniors to feel depressed and isolated. Even if a senior is surrounded by family, it's still important to establish and maintain peer relationships with people who share similar interests, hobbies and experiences.

Could singing folk songs be another secret to a long and happy life?

Chinese scholars have found a strong link between the communal singing of folk songs and living to a very old age. Their research into the unusually high percentage of centenarians in the county of Bama in Guangxi, China (which ranks fifth in the world for longevity), led them to discover a high correlation between longevity and participation in the local folk artists association. Whereas the expected factors of genetics, diet and exercise differed little between this region and others in rural China, folk singing stood out as a common denominator among the oldest of the old. The town of approximately 1,000 has a thousand-year history of traditional community singing, with a staged gathering to sing folk songs once every three to five days.

A connection between singing and healthy aging seems consistent with other research that links playing a musical instrument to healthy aging. Interestingly, memory studies have observed little or no decline for habitual or automatic forms of memory such as the ability to tie your shoes, drive your car or play a musical instrument. The cognitive process we call upon to recite lyrics is a linguistic exercise that stimulates the memory centers of the brain.

Chen Jinchao, one of the leaders of the study, believes that singing folk songs supports longevity because it involves seniors in a mutually beneficial social activity. It enables seniors to openly share and shed their anger and anxieties while giving them a sense of purpose.

Aging for a purpose

Another secret to living happily into older age is defining a reason to live. "Human beings thrive when their lives are imbued with purpose—a clear sense of who they are, why they are here, and where they are going," says University of Chicago psychologist Penny Visser. People lead their lives fulfilling specific roles, like student, employee, soldier, spouse, parent and so on. These roles are driven by expectations and goals. After retirement, the nebulous role of "senior citizen" is less demanding and less goal-oriented, Visser explains. As a result, seniors may experience fewer challenges that offer opportunities for mental or psychological growth.

In 2002, researchers at the Mayo Clinic found that optimistic people decreased their risk of early death by 50 percent compared with those who leaned more toward pessimism. Being positive is important, but even being present is an important step. Try not to let your mind wander toward the past or the future. Be fully here and enjoy what life has to offer in this moment; this appreciation will be uplifting and naturally cultivate happiness. If you want to age actively, it helps to find a purpose for living. Volunteering for a charitable organization is a great way to develop and maintain a sense of purpose, even if frailty or disability has limited your ability to accept "traditional" work.

Sleep well to age well

You might think that you need less sleep as you get older. Actually, seniors need as much sleep as younger adults—seven to nine hours per night. Sleep is essential to everyone's physical health and emotional well-being. Good sleep is also gaining recognition as one of the secrets to successful aging. The trouble is that seniors are prone to sleep disorders. In fact, one out of every two seniors suffers from some form of sleep deprivation.

"The biggest myth is that sleeping poorly is just part of getting old. Actually, seniors are falling asleep during the day because they aren't getting enough quality sleep at night," says Dr. Sonia Ancoli-Israel, Director of the Sleep Disorders Clinic at the San Diego Veterans Affairs Medical Center.

These results were presented at a 2008 sleep conference and were based on the study of 2,226 older female participants. Twenty-one percent of these women were determined to be "successful agers," based on their overall mental and physical health, social engagement and ability to live independently. Those women who were identified as successful agers tended to report less sleep disturbance on an insomnia rating scale than other women in the study. Women age 70 and older who sleep five hours or less per night may be more likely to experience falls than those who sleep seven to eight hours per night, according to a report in the September 8, 2008 issue of *Archives of Internal Medicine.*

Sadly, naps are not the answer to daytime drowsiness. Trying to catch up by napping during the day creates a sleep/wake cycle that interferes with normal sleep patterns. Here are a few things sleep experts recommend to help overcome insomnia:
- Stick to a regular sleep schedule, get up and go to bed at the same time each day.
- Stay active during the day, maintaining a moderate level of activity, especially outdoors. Studies show that people who experience natural daylight sleep better at night.
- Resist the urge to take naps during the day.

- Avoid consumption of caffeine and alcohol after sundown. Ending the ritual of a "night cap" will make the night more restful. Avoiding liquids before bedtime will also reduce your need to use the bathroom at night.
- Improve your sleep environment by keeping it quiet, dark and on the cool side.
- Check your mattress. An old or worn out mattress may be part of the problem.
- Sleep separately, in another room when necessary, if you share a bed with a partner who is restless, snores or has a chronic condition like coughing that keeps you awake.
- Check your medicines. Insomnia may be due to medications you are taking. If so, ask your doctor about substituting a different medication.

Know your hospital

Heart attacks, strokes, cancer and other acute illnesses are more survivable than ever. In fact, sicknesses that 20 years ago brought people's lives to a quick and certain end are now reduced to major life events that many experience and move past, living for many more decades. Nevertheless, a lot depends on the quality of care provided by the hospital. A 2009 study found that patients with the most common diagnoses who were treated in top-rated hospitals reduced their death risk by 27 percent. Patients who underwent surgery at these high-performing hospitals were also 8 percent less likely to suffer complications during their stay. (You can see how your local hospitals are rated, as well as which hospitals have been designated as Distinguished Hospitals for Clinical Excellence at websites like www.healthgrades.com.)

If you happen to have a major health issue or require surgery for any reason, your future quality of life—and your life itself—are in the hands of the hospital. That's obvious. What isn't obvious is what you can do to virtually guarantee you get the very best care.

Long-term care insurance = more options for care

One of the most important ways to ensure you enjoy the highest possible quality of life in your later years is to purchase long-term care insurance. Medical advances have taken the teeth out of the top three killers of people over 65—heart disease, cancer and diabetes. Survival rates are way up, and it looks like they're going to continue in that direction. The flip side of this decline of sudden death is that you're more likely to develop chronic illness, frailty and dementia. After all, aging itself is the leading factor for Alzheimer's and other persistent diseases. Care for these conditions is expensive. Health insurance and Medicare won't cover long-term care whereas long-term care insurance was designed to do just that.

Who should consider long-term care insurance?

Long-term insurance isn't for everyone. However, you should seriously consider it if you meet any of these conditions:

- You have assets like savings, investments or a home that you don't want to have to liquidate in order to pay for senior care.
- You want to keep from becoming dependent on your children or other family members
- You want to have the freedom to choose where you obtain senior care—such as in your home. (Without long-term care insurance, home care may not be affordable.)

Women especially should think seriously about long-term care insurance. Not only are woman more likely to outlive the men in their lives, they're also much more likely to provide care at home to an older relative. Statistics show that half of women (and one third of men) reaching the age of 65 will need long-term care before they die.

Middle age is the best time to look into buying long-term care insurance. If you wait until your 70s or 80s or until you get sick with a chronic illness, many insurers will consider you too risky. If you can get coverage at all, the premiums may be very expensive.

A good first step in educating yourself about long-term care insurance is to contact the Insurance Department in the community where you live and have them send you information on the regulations they have regarding long-term care insurance. Many local government agencies offer consumers basic protections, such as requiring coverage of Alzheimer's care and guaranteeing renewal as long as you pay your premiums on time. Also, your local area's agency on aging and the AARP may offer a list of companies that sell long-term care insurance policies. For more information on long-term care insurance, visit the National Association of Insurance Commissioners at www.naic.org or the American Association for Long-Term Care Insurance at www.aaltci.org.

REMEMBER...

Research on the lifestyle behaviors that contribute to a long and healthy lifespan have primarily focused on diet, physical activity and mental stimulation. Social interaction has only recently made headlines as a factor for an extended and more enjoyable lifespan. Whether from the companionship of a caregiver or friends and family, social interaction coupled with mental stimulation may hold the key to longevity. Also make the effort to get enough sleep, know the healthcare facilities in your area and determine whether long term care insurance is a sound investment for you and your family.

ELEVEN

What We Can Learn from the Oldest Living People on Earth: The Balanced Care Method™

The average life expectancy in developed countries currently hovers in the 70s and early 80s, but people can and do live much longer. "They will live no longer than 120 years" (Genesis 6:3) has often been taken as the outer reaches of the human body's longevity potential. But even 120 years may be an outdated benchmark.

Jeanne Clement is the longest living person in modern history. She was born February 21, 1875 and died August 4, 1997: 122 years and 164 days. At 14 she met Van Gogh. At 85 she learned to fence. At 100 she finally gave up riding a bicycle. At 114 she still walked freely. At 117 she quit smoking. What accounts for such extraordinary longevity? Madame Clement attributed her good health and long life to her copious use of olive oil in both her food and as a moisturizer. Other centenarians credit sensible eating, vices in moderation, regular exercise and simply the "Will of God."

There is no single explanation for how and why some people live so many healthier and more active years than others. But there is a place where more people live longer and healthier than any other place on earth: Okinawa, Japan. And recently scientists have been studying this group of seniors to see if we could learn to live a longer and more productive life.

The Okinawa Centenarian Study is based on the scientific findings over years of study by a group of physicians who moved to Okinawa to study this special population of seniors, 900 of whom are centenarians. One advantage of this study over some other studies on particularly long-lived populations is the reliability of record-keeping in Japanese prefectures since the 1870s that includes family registers as well a public census taken every five years.

Okinawa is an island prefecture of Japan in the East China Sea where the average life expectancy is just over 82 years (almost 78 for men and 86 for women). In a population of 1.3 million, there are more than 400 centenarians. That's about 34 per hundred thousand people. By comparison, there are currently between 5 and 10 people over 100 years old per hundred thousand in the United States. Thus, Okinawans are currently 3 to 7 times more likely to live to 102 than Americans.

As impressive as the long lives lived by the people of Okinawa are, what is of equal, if not more interest, is the quality of health most elders in Okinawa enjoy. Heart disease, cancer, dementia, diabetes and other conditions considered par for the course in older people in the West are rare in Okinawan elders.

Okinawan seniors have low cholesterol levels, low homocysteine levels and clear arteries, all of which reduces their risk of coronary heart disease by 80 percent compared to Western levels. It also keeps their stroke levels low. These clear arteries further help account for the fact that Okinawan seniors suffer from dementia at less than half the rate of Western populations.

There is also a low incidence of hormone-dependent cancers among Okinawan elders. They have 80 percent less breast cancer and prostate cancer and 50 percent less ovarian and colon cancers. Mammogram screenings are statistically unnecessary in Okinawa. Most older Okinawan men have never heard of prostate cancer and its symptoms. Plus, they experience slower rates of bone density loss, which helps them have 40 percent less hip fractures – a major cause of loss of mobility in older adults - than Westerners.

As if low heart disease and cancer rates and stronger bones and minds weren't enough, both Okinawan men and women maintain higher sex hormone levels than their Western counterparts as they age. Their levels of estrogen, testosterone, and DHEA (dehydroepiandrosterone) are all significantly higher. Since DHEA levels in particular tend to decline in direct proportion to age, the higher levels in Okinawan seniors suggest the seemingly impossible: They are *biologically* younger than Westerners of the same *chronological* age. Natural estrogen protects women against heart disease and bone density loss, and higher sex hormone levels in both sexes help maintain muscle mass, hair, libidos and other bodily functions.

While it can be easy to dismiss such a population as enjoying particularly healthy and long-living genetics, studies have found that such factors account for only about a third of the Okinawan seniors' extraordinary health and long lifespans. The rest? Lifestyle. Two-thirds of this enviable good health appears to be the result of diet, exercise, low stress levels, familial and community ties, social practices and spiritual beliefs. Each of these elements, just like the disorders and diseases they help prevent, feed on one another in a symbiotic relationship.

It's not all in the genes

Genetic factors are, undoubtedly, an important element in long-living populations. Different studies have found genetics to play anywhere from 10 to 33 percent of the role in determining lifespan in all animals. But most studies of human populations conclude that genetics determine about one-third of people's lifespan. While the results of studies of the seniors of Okinawa suggest that their genetics may play a role in the length of their lifespan, lifestyle factors have been found to play a much larger role than genetic factors in influencing how long a person – even a very long lived person – lives.

It is these lifestyle factors that inspired us to distill centuries of wisdom into an accessible program that family and professional caregivers could incorporate into the lives of the seniors they care for and that adults everywhere could observe to increase their chances of living Happy to 102.

This program is called the Balanced Care Method™ and it is based on the lifestyle factors that have led to such long and healthy lifespans in Okinawa: healthy diet, physical activity, sharp mind, social ties and purpose. Home Care Assistance caregivers throughout North America are trained in the Method, offering the first senior care solution with an emphasis on balance and longevity. By working with specific lifestyle behaviors, Home Care Assistance caregivers extend and enhance the lives of seniors, helping them live longer, happier, more balanced lives.

Dietary factors

A major factor in the extraordinary health enjoyed by Okinawa elders has been traced to their distinct diet. It is plant-based, high in fiber, low in protein, high in omega-3 fatty acids, and high in flavonoids. It includes low to moderate alcohol intake, contains plenty of fruits and vegetables, has very low levels of saturated fat and not too much salt. In essence, all of the features we discussed in our chapters on nutrition.

Okinawan seniors also engage in a practice of hara hachi bu. Hara hachi bu means eating until only 80 percent full. This naturally results in a low-calorie diet that, in turn, helps keep Okinawan slim throughout their lives, with a lean body mass (between 18 to 22 on the body mass index) and a low glycemic load (rate of blood sugars). One theory of aging sees human bodies much like cars: they run and run and run until they simply burn out and die. One of the main demands we make on our bodies is the consumption and digestion of food, a process that also leads to the production of free radicals, or unstable molecules. By limiting caloric intake, we limit how much food our bodies need to process and thus correspondingly decrease the amount of free radicals in our bloodstream. Okinawan seniors have low levels of free radicals in their blood, as well as low levels of lipid peroxides, a sign of less free radical-caused damage.

Eighty percent of the calories in their low-calorie diet are plant-based. They eat plenty of rice, a wide range of vegetables, fruits, sea vegetables and soy products. Of the 20 percent of animal-based calories they do consume, most of that is cold-water fish or stewed meats from which the fat has been rendered. The fats they eat – from fish, soy products, or cold-pressed canola oil – are largely mono-unsaturated or rich in omega-3 fatty acids. Alcohol drinking is moderate and sweets are occasional treats whereas green tea is sipped regularly.

There are many things about this diet that contribute to the long lives and good health of Okinawan. First of all, high fiber is a central pillar in many healthful diet guidelines. A high fiber diet helps maintain a sense of fullness that keeps people from overeating. It also aids in proper, efficient and pain-free digestion. Fiber comes from whole grains and fruits and vegetables. Grains and vegetables are complex carbohydrates (versus simple carbohydrates of refined flour and sugar) that break down slower and help maintain healthy glycemic loads, keeping the pancreas from taxing itself in efforts to produce enough insulin to process the spikes in blood sugar levels caused by eating excessive amounts of simple carbohydrates.

Along with providing fiber, the abundance of fruits and vegetables in the traditional Okinawan diet provides Okinawan seniors with lots of essential minerals and antioxidants, which fight free radicals in our systems. The Okinawan high-fiber, vegetable-laden diet is also low in protein.

The Western diet often includes 2, 3 or even 4 times as much protein as is needed on a daily basis. Much of this protein takes the form of meat and dairy products, which also contain saturated fat. Saturated fat, as the media and our doctors tell us, leads to unhealthy cholesterol levels and the production of artery-clogging homocysteine. When these higher levels of animal product consumption are combined with a lack of folate, an essential mineral found in dark, leafy green vegetables that helps to regulate homocysteine levels, the problem is compounded.

Furthermore, when we eat protein our bodies also need to process the by-products: ammonia and urea. Both of these toxins are processed through our kidneys, which are in turn dependent on the proper functioning of the liver. Too much protein puts a lot of pressure on a host of vital organs. The protein Okinawan seniors do eat tends to come from two sources: cold-water fish and soy. Each brings something to the ultra-healthy Okinawan diet.

Cold-water fish tends to be fatty, but that fat needs to stay liquid even in cold temperatures. Unlike other animal fats that solidify, the fat in cold-water fish remains free flowing. It is polyunsaturated and doesn't have the same artery-clogging properties as saturated fat and does have omega-3 fatty acids. Okinawans eat, on average, three servings of fish – mostly cold-water fish like mackerel, salmon and tuna – a week, leading to higher levels of omega-3 fatty acids in their systems than their counterparts in the West. And omega-3s are seemingly miracle workers: They are cancer-preventing, brain-function-enhancing and heart-protecting.

Okinawan seniors also eat several servings of soy products daily. Along with being an excellent source of low-fat protein, soy contains high levels of flavonoids. Flavonoids are strong antioxidants, fighting free radicals in any system they inhabit. Flavonoids also provide a source of natural, weak estrogens that can block the body's own estrogen in cases where the body's estrogens can cause cancer, a move that can prohibit hormone-induced cancers, particularly breast cancer and prostate cancer. In short, Okinawans high consumption of soy may explain their remarkable low rates of cancer.

It also explains the relative ease with which most Okinawan women go through menopause. The natural estrogen they get through their diet keeps hot flashes, mood swings and other menopausal symptoms to a minimum. It also helps maintain bone density and muscle mass, keeping older Okinawans looking, feeling and acting younger than one might expect from their age.

Antioxidants and flavonoids are also found in significant levels in tea, which Okinawan elders drink regularly in large amounts, keeping them hydrated and full of health-enhancing antioxidants and flavonoids.

The Okinawan diet is as remarkable for what it doesn't include as for what it does. Along with consuming limited red meat and almost no dairy products, low to moderate alcohol drinking helps further protect Okinawans. Some alcohol, especially when enjoyed with food, has been shown to have some health benefits. Yet alcohol increases the body's estrogen production, which can increase the possibility of developing hormone-dependent cancers. High alcohol consumption also destroys folates in the systems, which, as we saw above, are important players in maintaining heart health, avoiding stroke and promoting proper brain functioning.

Refined sugar and other sweets have a limited role in the traditional Okinawan diet. This helps Okinawans avoid blood sugar spikes, stress on the pancreas, empty calories and cravings for more of the same. Following the principle of eating until only 80 percent full is much easier when the foods one is eating are wholesome, nutritious and don't induce a physical desire to overeat.

Exercise factors

Okinawan seniors keep up their life-long routine of moderate exercise and physical activity that includes the three main groups of physical movement: flexibility, strength building and aerobic. Not that they think of it this way, they simply walk most places they go, keep up daily tasks like housework and gardening, practice the soft martial art of tai chi and work well past the age of "retirement." These are all low-impact, weight-bearing, moderate forms of physical activity. Tai chi alone provides its practitioners with aerobic, anaerobic and flexibility fitness.

Being physically fit helps keep Okinawan elders lean, healthy, and active. The particular activities they enjoy also give them a sense of psychological calmness.

Stress and lifestyle

The low-calorie, plant-based, omega-3-rich and flavonoid-laden diet and frequent, moderate, varied exercise enjoyed by Okinawan seniors sets them on a great path toward a healthy older age, but their remarkable lifespans and health can be further explained by the extent to which their lives are also low stress, socially rich and purposeful.

Pleasant lifestyle infuses all aspects of the Okinawan lifestyle. The dominant ease of living in Okinawa combines a society that celebrates the connection between present and past. It is a point of view that sees all people as good and emphasizes the importance of responsibility to and of individuals and groups. This offers Okinawan elders stress relief – well, actually protection from experiencing stress in the first place, which is even better – as well as a sense of social connection, better life satisfaction and sense of purpose, not to mention a respected, important role in their community.

In Okinawa helping your neighbor, caring for family, watching out for friends – are all part of daily life. Social networks on Okinawa help seniors live independently because social support is part of every stage of life.

The islands of Okinawa traditionally follow a relaxed pace, with slower rhythms and fewer "on the clock" commitments than are common in so many other modern societies. Being hurried, constantly worried or in a state of constant stress is not part of the Okinawan lifestyle. This behavior protects them from the negative physiological consequences of psychological stress: rapid heartbeat, frequent contraction and dilation of blood vessels, digestive problems and overworked glands. Since their immune systems aren't constantly being asked to fight stress created from being late or over-worked, they can focus on their real job: fighting disease. Of course, their healthful diet and regular exercise also help keep excess stress at bay.

A Westernized approach

A steady diet of mackerel, sweet potatoes and green tea is probably not realistic for most Westerners. Neither is a daily tai chi practice or walks between villages. Yet there are many ways to implement the principles of the Okinawan lifestyle within a Western framework. That is the foundation for the Balanced Care Method™.

The Balanced Care Method™ encourages a diet that mimics the practices of the Okinawan elders: high fiber, low-fat proteins, plenty of fresh fruits and vegetables, calcium-rich ingredients and omega-3-rich foods along with limited sweets and alcohol and plenty of hydrating water and tea. This high-fiber, plant-based diet is naturally low in calories, so "diets" in the weight-loss sense become unnecessary. And keep in mind, there is room in this diet profile for most people's favorite foods, at least in moderation.

Okinawan elders are much more physically active than their Western counterparts. The primary way the Balanced Care Method™ seeks to help seniors stay as active as possible is to encourage them to do as much as they can for themselves. Seniors who can still take walks, with companionship if necessary, are encouraged to do so on a regular basis. People interested in their gardens or doing light housework are supported to continue with help as needed. Hobbies, social visits and group activities are similarly facilitated.

The Balanced Care Method™ avoids the pitfalls of other forms of senior care, which often encourage dependency or make it difficult to maintain social ties or beloved hobbies because of transportation or space considerations. The more seniors can stick with their preferred activities and social networks, the more active, healthier and happier they can be. Continuing to attend places of worship, clubs and other groups echoes the social and connecting communal practices of the Okinawan elders.

The Balanced Care Method™ also makes it possible to have clients enjoy the outdoors on a regular basis. Fresh air, time in nature, sitting and enjoying a pretty view: These are all extraordinarily calming and stress-relieving for people of all ages and are particularly effective as people get older and lose their ability to relieve stress in other ways.

The Balanced Care Method™ is as much a way of seeing aging and understanding it as a part of a whole life, rich and meaningful at every stage, as it is a particular set of practices. Each element – fostering independence, encouraging the maintenance of social ties, remaining active physically and mentally – supports and reinforces the others. The best lesson we can learn from the seniors of Okinawa is to embrace and accept aging, to approach it with a sense of balance and calm. And, of course, to eat our vegetables.

Learn more at **BalancedCareMethod.com**

REMEMBER...

There is no single explanation for how and why some people live so many healthier and more active years than others. But there is a place where more people live longer and healthier than any other place on earth: Okinawa, Japan. In Okinawa, lifestyle factors have been found to play a much larger role than genetic factors in influencing how long a person lives. The Balanced Care Method™ is based on the lifestyle factors that have led to such long and healthy lifespans in Okinawa: healthy diet, physical activity, sharp mind, social ties and purpose. BalancedCareMethod.com

102 WAYS TO LIVE HAPPY TO 102

Healthy Diet

1. **Eat less and live longer.** Keep the 80 percent rule in mind, essentially not eating any more after you feel 80 percent full.

2. **Don't skip breakfast,** the easiest meal to skip and the most important.

3. **Eat a variety.** Eating a variety of fruits, vegetables, whole grains, lean proteins, dairy and omega-3 fats better ensures you get all the nutrients your body needs.

4. **Limit alcohol consumption,** since it can adversely affect alertness and coordination.

5. **Maintain an anti-inflammatory diet.** A diet high in fresh fruits and vegetables and minimally processed foods reduces inflammation in your body.

6. **Eat all natural.** Avoid high-calorie foods full of sugar, fat and artificial ingredients and concentrate on eating high-nutrient, high-flavor foods such as fruits, vegetables, herbs and spices.

7. **Drink tea.** Tea is a proven preventive treatment for hardening of the arteries and has potent antioxidant powers.

8. **Indulge your chocolate cravings.** Nutritionists recommend 60 percent or higher cocoa content; the darker, the better. Hot cocoa works, too!

9. **Know the flax.** Flax seeds benefit the heart and possess anti-cancer properties. They also lessen the severity of diabetes by stabilizing blood-sugar levels. Sprinkle it on everything in home cooking.

10. **Egg it on.** Eggs are a superior source of protein, containing all the essential amino acids needed by the human body.

11. **Go Nuts!** A handful of walnuts or almonds is all that's needed to combat heart disease and meet your daily omega-3 dietary recommendation.

12. **A carrot a day.** Nothing beats a carrot as a powerful source of beta-carotene. A single carrot (7 1/2" long) delivers 203 percent of the daily RDA for vitamin A.

13. **Be Blue.** Not only can blueberries lower your risk of heart disease and cancer, they are also anti-inflammatory. Frozen is as good as fresh.

14. **Eat more healthy fats.** Healthy fats to include in your diet are monounsaturated fats, found in vegetable oils, nuts, seeds and some plant foods as well as polyunsaturated fats, found in fatty fish and nuts.

15. **Avoid bad fats.** Bad fats include saturated fats, which are primarily derived from animal products, and trans fats, which are used in commercial fried foods, margarines and baked goods like cookies and crackers.

16. **Read labels.** Opt for products with at least three grams of fiber and low sugar content.

17. **Spice it up** with high-antioxidant spices and herbs such as cinnamon, ginger, curry, rosemary, thyme, oregano and red pepper.

18. **Drink up.** Drinking water throughout the day can decrease your urges for sweets, lower your cholesterol and blood pressure, minimize pain associated with arthritis, migraines, and colitis, hydrate your skin and help with digestion.

19. **Sideline the soda.** The phosphoric acid in carbonated beverages, particularly colas, can put you at risk for osteoporosis.

20. **Drink red wine.** Red wine is renowned for its many health benefits, primarily for the heart. New research from the Institute of Food suggests it may also protect you from potentially fatal food-borne pathogens.

21. **Marinate your meat.** Research from the Food Safety Consortium recommends marinades with rosemary, thyme, peppers, allspice, oregano, basil, garlic and onion to cut down on carcinogens.

22. **Eat "Brain food."** Keep your mind sharp by eating salmon, nuts, olive oil, soy, meat, eggs, dairy, leafy greens, beans, oatmeal and dark skinned fruits.

23. **Go green.** Eat organic, use eco-friendly products and practice green living to protect your health as well as the environment.

24. **Take supplements** in the form of a daily multi-vitamin and mineral supplement especially formulated for seniors.

Physical Activity

25. **Remain physically active** to improve balance, flexibility and strength, alleviate stress and depression, increase alertness and strengthen the heart and circulatory system.

26. **Keep it simple.** Even simple exercises such as stretching while in bed can improve the ability to stand, walk and even improve the reflexes needed to arrest impending falls.

27. **Warm up and cool down.** This is key to avoiding injury and reducing soreness.

28. **Commit to daily fitness.** Getting out there and staying active translates into better health and well-being – both physically and mentally.

29. **Commit to year-round exercise.** Don't quit your fitness routine because of inclement weather. Try new activities, such swimming at an indoor pool.

30. **Join a health club.** Be social and get fit. Two important factors to living Happy to 102!

31. **Stop smoking.**

32. **Count every step.** Wear a step counter throughout the day to count how many steps you take. One study showed that pedometer users increase their physical activity by 26.9 percent.

33. **Get aerobic.** Engage in moderate aerobic exercise frequently —3 to 5 times per week—for a total of 20 to 60 minutes each day.

34. **Break it up.** Instead of 20 or 30 minutes of exercise, break up your cardio into 10-minute segments throughout the day.

35. **Pump it up.** One pound of fat burns three calories a day while one pound of muscle burns 30 plus. Put a set of low-weight dumbbells by your television set – and use them!

36. **Challenge yourself.** To counteract age-related muscle loss, do exercises with progressively challenging resistance.

37. **Burn extra calories** by simply parking or having your caregiver park farther from your destinations.

38. **Take the stairs.** Rosemond Borboa, age 82, resident of Wyndham Retirement Center in Fresno, California says, "I eat three good meals a day and haven't gained any weight because I take the stairs."

39. **Posture.** See a chiropractor, physical therapist or post-rehabilitation specialist for postural exercises to reduce pain and risk of injury.

40. **Stretch.** A simple stretch involves bending your head to your shoulder holding it there and slowly bringing it back to the center and then switching sides.

41. **Head up.** Instead of holding your head to your shoulder while on the phone, get a headset and avoid injury to your neck and shoulders.

Sharp Mind

42. **Recall the events of the day.** Pay particular attention to the date and the headlines in the news. Review a few conversations for content and ideas. Recall what you had for breakfast and lunch.

43. **Memorize** phone numbers, names and word spellings.

44. **Visualize** some of the scenes that you have witnessed during the day each night.

45. **Recreate mental pictures.** Once or twice during every day, close your eyes and recreate a mental picture of what is 180 degrees behind you.

46. **Be artistic.** Look at an object – then look away and draw a rough likeness of it.

47. **Keep in touch** with what is current in movies, plays, books and music.

48. **Attend cultural events.** According to the American Academy of Neurology, cognitively active seniors are almost three times less likely to suffer dementia or develop Alzheimer's.

49. **Train your brain.** Working a daily crossword, Sudoku puzzle or another brain teasing game will improve your mental fitness. Even simple arithmetic problems can keep you sharp.

50. **A word a day.** Learn a new word each day and use it in conversation. Visit or have your caregiver visit websites like wordsmith.org for your daily word.

51. **Travel.** Join a senior elder hostel group and travel to local sights or travel the world for fun and mental stimulation. Take a caregiver for peace of mind.

52. **Music therapy.** Music can regulate mood, decrease aggression and depression, improve sleep and even create new brain cells.

Social Ties

53. **Stay social.** Join a club, have dinner with family and friends and do other activities with your social support network.

54. **Be tech savvy.** Stay connected by email and get involved in forums and chat rooms that interest you. Follow popular home care blogs like the one on HomeCareAssistance.com.

55. **Volunteer.** According to the AARP Bulletin, volunteering is good for brain health and gives you the opportunity to use your skills to contribute to the good of your community.

56. **Go out with the dog** for a walk at public parks.

57. **Participate in arts and crafts** with others, such as sewing circles or pottery classes.

58. **Join bridge clubs,** reading groups or other regular gatherings to establish a routine. Mental stimulation and social interaction combined is doubly beneficial!

59. **Take adult education** classes at the local college.

60. **Invite friends home**—your caregiver can help!

61. Attend worship services.

62. Attend a local performance or sporting event, such as high school or college plays, concerts or sports outings.

63. Take trips to the salon to have hair and nails done.

64. Become involved in political campaigns or social causes.

Calmness & Purpose

65. Smile. Smiling lowers blood pressure, heart rate and the stress hormone cortisol.

66. Humor your stress. Laughing improves circulation, lowers blood pressure, releases tension and improves your immune system.

67. Think positive. If you can't change the situation, change the way you think about it.

68. Let nature take your stress away. Simply being outdoors with green plants, fresh air and the sounds of nature is a proven stress buster.

69. Practice Yoga. The Mayo Clinic recommends practicing yoga to reduce stress and anxiety.

70. **Begin with breathing.** Consciously focusing on your breath keeps you in the moment.

71. **Aromatherapy.** Try lavender, lemongrass, cinnamon or cedarwood.

72. **Live with your senses.** Aim to hear, feel, see, smell and taste all of life's nuances.

73. **Take time outs.** They worked when you were little and they can work now to reduce stress now and increase mental and physical energy.

74. **Accept yourself** as you are at any age.

75. **Be true to yourself.** Dr. John Izzo, author of The Five Secrets You Must Discover Before You Die, explains, "Being true to yourself often means drowning out other voices that would ask you to live their dreams instead of yours."

76. **Give love.** The choice to give love is even more important in determining happiness than receiving it.

77. **Live the moment.** You have no power over the past and little power over the future so replace your sad dwellings of the past and fears of the future with a priority to appreciate and live in the present.

78. Give more than you take. It is what you give, not what you take that gives life meaning.

79. Love your family. This can keep you feeling young in heart and body.

80. Love yourself, now and on the journey to 102.

Basic Health and Safety

81. Have eyes checked by an eye doctor at least once a year. Vision changes, as well as eye diseases like glaucoma and macular degeneration, can progress rapidly as people age, making it difficult to notice hazards when walking.

82. Consider a hearing aid to avoid the social isolation that results from difficulty in hearing the conversations taking place around you.

83. Protect your eyes. Four (protected) eyes are better than two. Wear eye glasses with an anti-reflective coating to improve your vision.

84. Block the sun. Wear sunscreen, sunglasses and a hat for sun protection and to reduce glare that could cause a fall. Exposure to direct sunlight has also been found to cause or aggravate cataracts.

85. **Monitor medications.** You or your caregiver should use a log to keep track of your medications. Learn their side effects, especially if they affect alertness or balance, as tranquilizers do. It's best to limit or avoid physical activities when under the effects of such medications.

86. **Schedule regular checkups.** Even if you are feeling fine, it's important to have regular physical, vision and hearing exams. Eyeglasses and hearing aids should be worn as instructed and have the most up-to-date prescription.

87. **Use proper equipment.** A doctor, physical therapist or a medical equipment supplier can help you choose the best cane, walker or wheelchair. A power assisted seat-lift chair may be a wise furniture investment.

88. **Dress for safety.** Safety starts with sturdy shoes. Nonskid soles, flat bottoms and good support are essential.

89. **Take medications as they are prescribed.** Clearly label your medications and follow the instructions.

90. **Keep emergency numbers handy.** When a crisis occurs, the quicker you can get help, the better. And, for when all is peaceful, the security you get from knowing you're well-prepared is invaluable.

91. **Wear your seatbelt.**

92. **Brush and floss your teeth.** According to research in Circulation, chronic inflammation caused by periodontal disease has been linked to cardiovascular disease and Alzheimer's.

93. **Turn it down.** According to the House Ear Institute, noise-induced hearing loss is a leading cause of permanent hearing loss that can be prevented by turning down the volume on your television, radio or headsets to a level that you can comfortably hear.

94. **Practice healthy sleeping habits.** Not getting enough nightly rest puts you at risk for accidents, depression and other illnesses. Improve your sleep environment by keeping it quiet, dark and on the cool side.

95. **Check your mattress.** If you have trouble sleeping, an old or worn out mattress may be part of the problem.

96. **Ensure your home is safe.** Make sure you or your caregiver follows the tips from Chapter 4 to maintain a safe home environment. Or contact a home safety professional about a formal evaluation.

97. **Clear the clutter.** Reduce falls by keeping all walking area clear and arranging furniture to avoid blockage.

98. **Install smoke alarms** and check them monthly.

99. **Hire a home care agency** to care for your parents, your patients or you. Visit HomeCareAssistance.com

100. **Give up driving** or take away the keys when the warning signs (Chapter 4) indicate it's time and hire a caregiver to provide transportation services.

101. **Hire a sitter.** Hire a hospital sitter next time you or a family member checks in to the hospital, for extra attention and companionship.

102. **Live the Balanced Care Method™.** Obtain more information at BalancedCareMethod.com or visit HomeCareAssistance.com for in-home care from caregivers trained **in** the Method.

HappyTo102.com